FINANCIAL
Statements

workbook

NVQ LEVEL 4
ACCOUNTING

Derek Street

Consultants: David Cox, Michael Fardon
and Roger Petheram

Published by Osborne Books Limited
Unit 1B Everoak Estate
Bromyard Road
Worcester WR2 5HP
Tel 01905 748071
Email books@osbornebooks.co.uk
Website www.osbornebooks.co.uk

Cover and page design by Hedgehog

Printed by the Bath Press, Bath

British Library Cataloguing in Publication Data
A catalogue record for this book is available from the British Library

ISBN 1 872962 68 8

CONTENTS

How to use this book

NVQ competences

1 **chapter activities**

2 **assignments**

3 Central Assessment tasks

ACKNOWLEDGEMENTS

Osborne Books would like to thank the author Derek Street for providing the basis of the activities and also the consulting team – David Cox, Michael Fardon and Roger Petheram – for reading and editing the text and for writing further activities. The publisher would also like to thank the following for their help with the editing and production of the book: Catherine and Robert Fardon, Rosemarie Griffiths and Jon Moore.

Thanks are particularly due to the Association of Accounting Technicians for their generous permission for the reproduction and adaptation of Central Assessment material throughout the book and also to the Lead Body for Accounting for permission to reproduce extracts from the Standards of Competence for Accounting.

AUTHOR

Derek Street has had over fifteen years' experience of teaching accountancy students, including the AAT qualification at all three levels. His lecturing experience has been gained at Evesham College of FE, Gloucester College of Arts and Technology (GLOSCAT) and North East Worcestershire College where he is currently Head of Department, Professional Studies.

HOW TO USE THIS BOOK

Financial Statements Workbook is designed to be used alongside Osborne Books' *Financial Statements Tutorial* and is ideal for student use in the classroom, at home and on distance learning courses. Both the Tutorial and the Workbook are designed for students preparing for assessment for Unit 11 'Drafting Financial Statements (Accounting Practice, Industry and Commerce)'.

Financial Statements Workbook is divided into three sections: chapter activities, assignments and Central Assessment Tasks.

chapter activities

Chapter activities are self-contained exercises which are designed to supplement the activities in the tutorial text. The activities – some of which are adapted AAT Central Assessment Tasks – are generally more extended than the exercises in the tutorial and provide useful practice for students preparing for assessment away from the classroom. There are activities relating to each chapter of the tutorial text.

assignments

The assignments in this section, which include some adapted AAT Central Assessment Tasks, are intended to be used as students progress through the course, to consolidate learning and to provide practice in Central Assessment technique. Each assignment covers two related chapters – with the exception of Assignment 6 which covers Chapter 11, Consolidated Accounts. The chapters of the tutorial text covered by each assignment are listed in the assignment summary on page 87.

Central Assessment Tasks

Osborne Books is grateful to the AAT for their kind permission for the reproduction and adaptation of selected tasks from past Central Assessments in this Section. Some names and numbers have been changed to maintain consistency of presentation. The principal objective of this section is to develop technique in tackling Central Assessment tasks. Students should be discouraged from 'question spotting' as it is important that the whole range of the specification is covered.

answers

Answers are not provided in the text. A Tutor Pack is available separately. Please telephone Osborne Books on 01905 748071 for details or refer to the AAT pages on www.osbornebooks.co.uk

NVQ COMPETENCES

Unit 11: DRAFTING FINANCIAL STATEMENTS (ACCOUNTING PRACTICE, INDUSTRY AND COMMERCE)

element 1

interpret financial statements

- *the general purpose of financial statements used in various organisations is identified*
- *elements of financial statements used in various organisations are identified*
- *the relationship of elements within financial statements is identified*
- *the relationship between elements of limited company financial statements is interpreted*
- *unusual features or significant issues are identified within financial statements*
- *valid conclusions are drawn from the information contained within financial statements*
- *conclusions and interpretations are clearly presented*

element 2

draft limited company, sole trader and partnership year end financial statements

- *financial statements are accurately drafted from the appropriate information*
- *subsequent adjustments are correctly implemented*
- *draft accounts comply with domestic standards and legislation and, where relevant, partnership agreement*
- *a cash flow statement is correctly prepared and interpreted where required*
- *year end financial statements are presented for approval to the appropriate person in clear form*
- *confidentiality procedures are followed at all times*
- *the organisation's policies, regulations, procedures and timescales relating to financial statements are observed at all times*
- *discrepancies, unusual features or queries are identified and either resolved or referred to the appropriate person*

Section 1

Chapter activities

This section contains activities which are suitable for use with the individual chapters of 'Financial Statements Tutorial' from Osborne Books.

PURPOSE OF FINANCIAL STATEMENTS

1.1 Which of the following cannot be described as a private sector organisation?

(a)   A public corporation

(b)   A sole trader

(c)   A partnership

(d)   A public limited company

1.2 Which of the following statements is correct?

	Assets	*Liabilities*	*Ownership interest*
	£	£	£
(a)	30,500	10,250	40,750
(b)	17,250	31,500	14,250
(c)	22,300	10,100	16,500
(d)	26,450	10,850	15,600

1.3 Which of the following represents a key objective for the public sector?

(a)   Profit

(b)   Best value

(c)   Dividends for shareholders

(d)   Increased market share

1.4 Which of the following statements best describes the accounting concept of going concern?

(a)   Expenses and revenues are matched to the same time period in which they relate.

(b)   The business will continue to trade for the foreseeable future.

(c)   When a business produces its financial statements it should always adopt a conservative figure for profit and/or the valuation of its assets.

(d)   Items with a low value should not be reported separately in the financial accounts.

1.5   Identify the main objectives of financial statements.

1.6   Briefly explain the following concepts which are used in accountancy:

(a)   Materiality

(b)   Consistency

1.7   A statement of accounting principles has been developed by the Accounting Standards Board. Explain the reasons why there has been a need to devise such a statement.

1.8   The accounting equation of a business is as follows:

Assets £2,000 – Liabilities £1,200 = Ownership interest £800

The business subsequently makes two transactions:

(1)   it purchases stock for £250 cash, and

(2)   it sells the stock purchased in (1) on credit for £350

Required:

(a)   Explain what each of the terms 'assets', 'liabilities' and 'ownership interest' means.

(b)   Explain the effect of each of the two transactions on the elements in the balance sheet.

(c)   State the accounting equation for the business after the two transactions have taken place.

(d)   Draft a simple profit and loss account for the two transactions.

(e)   Give an example of a user who might be interested in a profit and loss account. Describe one type of decision which might be made by the user based on information in the profit and loss account.

2 SOLE TRADER FINAL ACCOUNTS

2.1 Which of the following statements is used to calculate net profit?

(a) A Trial Balance

(b) A Trading Account

(c) A Balance Sheet

(d) A Profit and Loss Account

2.2 Which of the following statements best describes working capital?

(a) The excess of Fixed Assets over Long-term Liabilities

(b) The excess of Current Assets over Long-term Liabilities

(c) The excess of Current Assets over Current Liabilities

(d) The excess of Fixed Assets over Current Liabilities

2.3 In the balance sheet of a sole trader, prepayments should be shown under which of the following headings?

(a) Fixed Assets

(b) Current Assets

(c) Current Liabilities

(d) Long-term Liabilities

2.4 Distinguish between bad debts and doubtful debts.

2.5 Explain the difference between long-term liabilities and capital.

2.6 What is the difference between an accrual and a prepayment and how do they affect the financial statements?

2.7 Identify the two main statements which comprise the final accounts of a sole trader. Give examples of the main headings contained within each statement.

2.8 The following trial balance has been extracted from the books of account of Mr Malcolm Nash, a sole trader who trades as Nash insurance.

Nash Insurance: trial balance as at 31 March 20-7

	Dr £	Cr £
Sales		138,000
Rent rates and insurance	7,800	
Postage and stationery	9,600	
Advertising	3,000	
Salaries and wages	32,300	
Motor expenses	12,600	
Sales commission paid	22,200	
Bad debts written off	2,400	
Debtors	12,800	
Creditors		8,400
Cash at Bank	3,800	
Stock of stationery as at 1 April 20-6	2,500	
Drawings	25,600	
Office and Computer equipment at cost	58,000	
Motor Vehicles at cost	70,000	
Accumulated depreciation as at 1 April 20-6		
Office & Computer equipment		23,200
Motor Vehicles		42,000
Capital		51,000
	262,600	262,600

Additional information as at 31 March 20-7

(a) Rent is accrued by £2,200

(b) Advertising has been prepaid by £750

(c) Stock of stationery at the close of business amounted to £3,250 at cost

(d) Depreciation policy is as follows:
Office and Computer equipment   10% on cost
Motor vehicles   20% on cost

REQUIRED

Task 1

Prepare a profit and loss account for the year ended 31 March 20-7.

Task 2

Prepare a balance sheet as at 31 March 20-7.

2.9 You have been asked to assist in the preparation of the financial statements of Russell Salter who runs a ceramics and pottery business. His book-keeper has produced an extended trial balance as at 31 March 20-2. This is set out on the next page.

The following information is also available for the current year.

1   Stock has been counted on 31st March 20-2, and was valued at cost at £98,600. The valuation includes a consignment of Aztec plant pots which cost £4,000 to buy in. Some of these pots have now been damaged when they were moved by the fork lift truck. As a consequence the net realisable value of the pots is now £2,400.

2   After the year end, a customer whose year end balance was £2,500 went into bankruptcy, and you are now required to write off the debt as irrecoverable.

3   The new provision for bad and doubtful debts needs to be adjusted to 5% of the closing debtors balances (after consideration of point 2 above).

REQUIRED

Task 1

Draft a profit and loss account for Russell Salter for the year ended 31 March 20-2 incorporating the adjustments 1-3 above.

Task 2

Draft a balance sheet as at 31 March 20-2.

EXTENDED TRIAL BALANCE name: Russell Salter   date: 31st March 20-2

Description	Ledger balances		Adjustments		Profit and loss		Balance sheet	
	Dr £	Cr £	Dr £	Cr £	Dr £	Cr £	Dr £	Cr £
Drawings	43,000						43,000	
Heat and Light	3,520		280		3,800			
Purchases	324,860				324,860			
Sales		514,700				514,700		
Debtors ledger control account	82,000						82,000	
Furniture and Fittings at cost	56,000						56,000	
Motor Vehicles at cost	33,000						33,000	
Bad debts written off	1,080				1,080			
Returns outwards		14,920				14,920		
Capital as at 1.4.20-1		88,160						88,160
Stock	87,400				87,400			
Rent, rates and Insurance	17,000		200	800	16,400			
Accumulated dep'n – Furniture and Fittings		24,000		6,400				30,400
– Motor Vehicles		12,600		4,080				16,680
Bank charges and Interest	640				640			
Cash at Bank	3,600						3,600	
Creditors ledger control account		92,000						92,000
Depreciation expense – Furniture & Fittings			6,400		6,400			
Depreciation expense – Motor Vehicles			4,080		4,080			
Carriage Inwards	2,640				2,640			
Returns inwards	6,700				6,700			
Postage, Stationery and Telephone	5,820			320	5,500			
Wages and Salaries	78,840		360		79,200			
Carriage Outwards	1,700				1,700			
Prepayments			1,120				1,120	
Accruals				840				840
Discounts allowed	980				980			
Provision for doubtful debts		2,400						2,400
Net profit/loss						11,760	11,760	
	748,780	748,780	12,440	12,440	541,380	541,380	230,480	230,480

2.10 The latest trial balance of Salim Anwar, who runs a haberdashery business is shown below. You have been asked to assist in the preparation of his financial statements for the year ended 31 July 20-2.

	Dr	Cr
	£	£
Land and Buildings at cost	140,000	
Delivery van at cost	32,000	
Shop Fittings at cost	62,000	
Accumulated Depreciation as at 01.08.01		
– Premises		16,800
– Delivery van		11,520
– Shop Fittings		24,800
Drawings	42,800	
Stock at 01.08.01	33,260	
Carriage Inwards	2,990	
Cash in hand	500	
Bank		4,160
Creditors		19,180
Discounts received		4,770
Capital		161,590
Bank Loan Account		15,000
Sales		208,630
HMCE (VAT account)		8,940
Purchases	112,590	
Delivery van expenses	7,220	
Shop expenses	8,210	
Heat and Light	2,640	
Postage, Stationery and Telephone	1,010	
Wages and salaries	18,720	
Advertising	3,910	
Business Rates and insurance	2,460	
Shop Repairs	5,080	
	475,390	475,390

Further information

1   Closing stock has been counted and valued at £51,840.

2   Depreciation charges for the year are based upon the following annual policy rates:

        Land and Buildings 2% on cost (straight line method)

        Delivery Van 20% on the reducing balance method

        Shop Fittings 10% on cost (straight line method)

3   A further £840 is owed for heat and light and should now be accrued for.

4   During the year Salim took goods for his own use and for presents for the family, totalling £850 at cost.

5   Business Rates prepaid amounted to £610 as at 31 July 20-2.

REQUIRED

Task 1

Draft a profit and loss account for Salim Anwar for the year to 31 July 20-2, incorporating points 1 – 5 above.

Task 2

Prepare Salim Anwar's balance sheet as at 31 July 20-2.

2.11 You have been asked by Sandro Venus to assist in the preparation of the year-end financial statements of his business. He is a sole trader who runs a trading business which specialises in ornaments decorated with sea shells. The extended trial balance as at 31 March 20-7 is set out on the next page.

You are given the following further information:

(a)   A general provision for doubtful debts is to be set up at 5 per cent of the year-end debtors' balance.

(b)   During the year Sandro Venus took goods which had cost £500 for his own personal use in decorating his flat.

(c)   At the end of the year, one of the motor vehicles which had cost £5,500 and on which there was accumulated depreciation of £2,400 was sold for £3,500. Payment for the vehicle sold has not yet been received by Sandro Venus and no entry to reflect the sale has been made in the extended trial balance.

REQUIRED

Task 1

Make any additional adjustments you feel necessary to the balances in the extended trial balance as a result of the matters set out in the further information above. Set out your adjustments in the form of journal entries.

Note: Narratives are not required.

Task 2

Draft a profit and loss account for the year ended 31 March 20-7.

EXTENDED TRIAL BALANCE name: Sandro Venus date: 31st March 20-7

Description	Trial balances Dr £	Trial balances Cr £	Adjustments Dr £	Adjustments Cr £	Profit and loss Dr £	Profit and loss Cr £	Balance sheet Dr £	Balance sheet Cr £
Wages and National Insurance Contributions	28,996		348		29,344			
Capital as at 1 April 20-6		83,696						83,696
Postage and stationery	524				524			
Accumulated dep'n – motor vehicles		8,125		6,094				14,219
Accumulated dep'n – office equipment		1,375		1,375				2,750
Accumulated dep'n – fixtures and fittings		2,780		2,780				5,560
Purchases	103,742				103,742			
Trade creditors		17,725						17,725
Carriage inwards	923				923			
Motor vehicles (cost)	32,500						32,500	
Office equipment (cost)	13,745						13,745	
Fixtures & fittings (cost)	27,800						27,800	
Sales		187,325				187,325		
Returns outwards		1,014				1,014		
Trade debtors	18,740						18,740	
Drawings	14,400						14,400	
Depreciation – motor vehicles			6,094		6,094			
Depreciation – office equipment			1,375		1,375			
Depreciation – fixtures and fittings			2,780		2,780			
Prepayments			320				320	
Accruals				1,131				1,131
Stock	27,931		30,229	30,229	27,931	30,229	30,229	
Returns inwards	1,437				1,437			
Cash at bank	9,473						9,473	
Cash in hand	166						166	
Bank deposit interest		972				972		
Carriage outwards	657				657			
Rent, rates and insurance	8,041			320	7,721			
Bad debts	830				830			
Discounts allowed	373				373			
Bank charges	693				693			
Telephone	3,524		783		4,307			
Lighting and heating	3,755				3,755			
Motor expenses	4,762				4,762			
Profit					22,292			22,292
	303,012	303,012	41,929	41,929	219,540	219,540	147,373	147,373

2.12   Elizabeth Ogier has asked you to assist in the preparation of the year-end financial statements of her wholesale perfume business. The trial balance as at 30 September 20-9 is set out below:

Elizabeth Ogier
Trial Balance as at 30 September 20-9

	Debit	Credit
	£	£
Purchases	113,565	
Rent, rates and insurance	8,291	
Motor expenses	5,813	
Bad debts	1,420	
Drawings	24,000	
Trade debtors	38,410	
Trade creditors		18,928
Capital as at 1 October 20-8		83,707
Sales		230,461
Returns outwards		2,911
Carriage inwards	1,256	
Returns inwards	3,053	
Carriage outwards	1,571	
Salespersons' commission	2,561	
Bank charges	710	
Depreciation – office equipment	2,312	
Depreciation – fixtures and fittings	602	
Stock as at 1 October 20-8	46,092	
Motor vehicles at cost	36,000	
Office equipment at cost	11,560	
Fixtures and fittings at cost	6,019	
Accumulated depreciation – motor vehicles		18,360
Accumulated depreciation – office equipment		3,825
Accumulated depreciation – fixtures and fittings		1,352
Wages, salaries and National Insurance contribution	47,564	
Lighting and heating	3,056	
Postage and stationery	1,037	
Telephone	3,571	
Cash at bank	2,131	
Cash in hand	102	
Accruals		1,562
Discounts allowed	410	
	361,106	361,106

Further information

- The stock at the close of business on 30 September 20-9 was valued at cost at £49,477. However, included in this balance were some goods which had cost £8,200 but it is estimated that they could now be sold for only £4,800.

- Included in the rent, rates and insurance balance is a payment of £1,200 which relates to rent for the period from 1 October 20-9 to December 20-9.

- The purchases figure includes goods to the value of £2,000 which Elizabeth took from the business for personal use and for gifts to friends.

- Although depreciation for office equipment and fixtures and fittings has been calculated and charged for the year, no depreciation has been calculated or charged for motor vehicles. Motor vehicles are depreciated using the reducing balance method at a rate of 30 per cent per annum.

REQUIRED

Task 1

Make any additional adjustments you feel necessary to the balances in the trial balance as a result of the matters set out in the further information above. Set out your adjustments in the form of journal entries.

Note: Narratives are not required.

Task 2

Draft a profit and loss account for the year ended 30 September 20-9.

3 PARTNERSHIP FINAL ACCOUNTS

3.1 Jackson and Pollock are in partnership together, investing £60,000 and £80,000 of their own capital respectively. The partnership agreement stipulates the following:

	Jackson	Pollock
Partners' salary	£16,000	£12,000
Interest on Capital (per annum)	10%	10%
Partners' share of profits/losses	60%	40%

If the partnership makes a net profit of £90,000 what would be the total profit (including salary and interest on capital) receivable by Pollock?

(a) £50,800

(b) £39,200

(c) £46,800

(d) £41,200

3.2 In the absence of a partnership agreement which of the following statements is correct?

(a) Partners share profits in proportion to their original capital contributions and interest on capital is payable at 5%.

(b) Partners share profits equally and interest on capital is payable at 5%.

(c) Partners share profits in proportion to their original capital contributions but no interest on capital is payable.

(d) Partners share profits equally and no interest is payable.

3.3 What is the correct double entry for the allocation of a partnership salary?

(a) Debit profit and loss appropriation account
Credit current account

(b) Debit current account
Credit profit and loss appropriation account

(c) Debit profit and loss appropriation account
Credit capital account

(d) Debit capital account
Credit profit and loss appropriation account.

3.4 Aldridge and Prior are in partnership investing capital of £100,000 and £140,000 each respectively. The partnership agreement stipulates the following for the year:

	Aldridge	Prior
Interest on drawings	£2,500	£1,500
Partners' salaries	£35,000	£30,000
Interest on Capital (per annum)	15%	15%
Share of profits/losses	40%	60%

If the net profit for the year was £50,000 what would be the total profit (including salary and interest on drawings and capital) receivable by Aldridge?

(a)   £21,300

(b)   £33,700

(c)   £28,700

(d)   £54,500

3.5   Brian, Raul and Lafta are in partnership, sharing profits and losses equally. For the year ending 30 September 20-9, the following details apply: Raul is entitled to salary of £12,000 and interest on capital is payable as shown below:

	£
Brian	15,000
Raul	10,000
Lafta	12,000

If the net profit for the year is £106,000, show the partnership appropriation account for the same period.

3.6   Gilbert and Sullivan are in partnership sharing profits in the ratio of 3:2. For the year ending 31 August 20-8 the following details apply.

	Salaries	Interest on Drawings	Interest on Capital
	£	£	£
Gilbert	12,650	2,450	18,600
Sullivan	18,350	1,950	15,200

The balances brought forward in the current accounts from last year's balance sheet show Gilbert has a £10,700 credit balance and Sullivan a £2,200 debit balance. The partnership recorded a net profit of £45,000 during the year.

Reconstruct Sullivan's current account for the year, taking into account the information given above.

3.7   In partnership accounts why is

(a)   interest paid on capital?

(b)   interest charged to partners' on drawings?

3.8   What are the main disadvantages which need to be considered when converting a sole trader business into a partnership?

3.9 Miquel, Nasser and Edwina are in partnership together trading as a firm of financial consultants. You have been asked to finalise the partnership accounts for the year ended 30 September 20-2.

The trainee accountant has given you the following draft information:

The profit for the year ended 30 September 20-2 amounted to £318,360.

The partners are entitled to the following annual salaries:

	£
Miquel	42,000
Nasser	36,000
Edwina	32,000

Interest on Capital is to be paid at a rate of 8% on the balance at the beginning of the year on the capital accounts. No interest is to be paid on current account balances.

Cash drawings for the year amounted to;

	£
Miquel	93,000
Nasser	84,000
Edwina	71,000

The balances on the capital and current accounts as at 1 October 20-1 were as follows:

	Capital Accounts	Current Accounts
	£	£
Miquel	86,000	8,750 cr.
Nasser	69,000	4,450 dr.
Edwina	57,000	7,860 dr.

The profit sharing ratios in the partnership currently are

Miquel	3/8
Nasser	3/8
Edwina	2/8

REQUIRED

Task 1
Prepare the partnership appropriation account for the year ended 30 September 20-2.

Task 2
Prepare the partners' current accounts for the year ended 30 September 20-2

3.10 Britain and Simpson trade as a partnership. Their partnership agreement provides for the following:

- Interest on fixed capital contributions at 8% per annum. No interest is to be charged on drawings or allowed or charged on current account balances.

- The partners are to receive the following annual salaries:

Britain	£25,000
Simpson	£20,000

• Profits and losses are to be shared as follows:

Britain   60%

Simpson   40%

The following trial balance has been extracted from the ledger of the partnership as at 31 May 20-6. You are required to complete the annual accounts for the year

	Dr £	Cr £
Business Premises at cost	250,000	
Office Equipment at cost	100,000	
Motor Vehicles	86,000	
Provision for depreciation as at 1 June 20-5		
– Business Premises		15,000
– Office Equipment		20,000
– Motor Vehicles		17,200
Stock as at 1 June 20-5	31,690	
Purchases	235,900	
Sales		655,400
Telephone and Communication expenses	14,250	
Postage and Stationery costs	3,760	
Repairs and renewals to premises	2,840	
Office expenses	5,990	
Wages and Salaries	135,720	
Motor expenses	6,780	
General expenses	15,660	
Cleaning costs	6,190	
Trade debtors	59,600	
Trade creditors		38,700
Cash at bank and in hand	11,590	
Drawings:		
– Britain	33,900	
– Simpson	28,600	
Capital Accounts		
– Britain		160,000
– Simpson		100,000
Current Accounts		
– Britain		6,280
– Simpson	4,110	
Loan Account – Britain		20,000
	1,032,580	1,032,580

Additional information

Stock at the close of business on 31 May 20-6 has been valued at £34,960

Interest on the Partners' loan account is payable at 10% per annum

Fixed Assets are depreciated at the following annual percentage rates:

Business Premises	3% on cost
Office Equipment	10% on cost
Motor vehicles	20% based on the reduced balance method

REQUIRED

Task 1

Prepare the trading, profit and loss and appropriation account for the year ended 31 May 20-6.

Task 2

Prepare the partnership balance sheet as at 31 May 20-6.

3.11 You are working in the business services department of a firm of Chartered Accountants. A partnership, Shaw and Turner, has approached your firm for assistance in preparing its financial statements. Shaw and Turner commenced activities on 1 April 20-3 when P Shaw, an established retailer in a small town north of Manchester, entered into partnership with B Turner.

A colleague in your firm has already produced a draft profit and loss account and a draft balance sheet for the partnership for the year ended 31 March 20-4 but has become unwell and is unable to complete all the entries required and finalise the financial statements. You have been asked to complete the task.

From the file of information left by your colleague you have discovered that a net profit of £52,530 had been made by the partnership according to the draft profit and loss account. No appropriation account or partners' current accounts had yet been completed and some adjustment may be necessary to the draft net profit figure.

Your colleague has left a memorandum with the following information which may be relevant.

(a)   P Shaw made a loan to the partnership on 1 April 20-3 of £10,000. Interest on the loan is to be credited to P Shaw at a rate of 12.5 per cent per annum.

(b)   The partners are to be credited with annual salaries as follows:

P Shaw   £20,000

B Turner   £10,000

(c)   The partners are to be credited with interest on their capital account balances at the rate of 10 per cent per annum.

(d)   The balances of net profits and losses are to be shared between P Shaw and B Turner in the proportions three fifths and two fifths respectively.

(e)   The partners have made the following drawings during the year:

   P Shaw   £16,700

   B Turner   £22,300

(f)   Separate capital accounts and current accounts are to be maintained for each partner. The balances on the capital accounts at 31 March 20-4 as shown in the draft statements are as follows:

   P Shaw   £34,000

   B Turner   £24,000

REQUIRED

Task 1

Draw up the appropriation account for the partnership of Shaw and Turner for the year ended 31 March 20-4.

Task 2

Prepare the partners' current accounts for the year ended 31 March 20-4.

4 CHANGES IN PARTNERSHIPS

4.1 Keith, Liam and Mark are in partnership with Capital of £50,000 each. They currently share profits and losses in the ratio of 3:2:1 respectively. The business premises are currently recorded at their net book value which is at cost £250,000 less accumulated depreciation of £25,000. They now wish to revalue the premises at its current market valuation of £345,000. After the revaluation, the capital of Liam will be:

(a)   £110,000

(b)   £90,000

(c)   £70,000

(d)   £50,000

4.2 Norman, Oliver and Peter are in partnership sharing profits in the ratio of 3:2:1 respectively. Each has a fixed capital contribution of £75,000. Quentin joins the business as a new partner, introducing £80,000 capital. In the new business the profit shares will be Norman (3) Oliver (2) Peter (1) and Quentin (1). An adjustment is made for goodwill on the introduction of Quentin to the value of £42,000, but no goodwill is to be left in the books of account after his admission. What will be the balance on Oliver's capital account after the introduction and elimination of goodwill?

(a)   £73,000

(b)   £75,000

(c)   £77,000

(d)   £82,000

4.3 In a partnership dissolution, any loss on realisation is allocated between the partners in accordance with:

(a)   The balance on the partners capital accounts

(b)   The balance on the partners current accounts

(c)   The balances on both the capital and current accounts

(d)   The partnership profit sharing ratios

4.4 According to the Garner v Murray (1904) ruling any insolvent partners' deficiency should be allocated to the remaining solvent partners according to the agreed:

(a)   Capital accounts

(b)   Current accounts

(c)   Capital and current accounts

(d)   Profit sharing ratios

4.5 The balance sheet of a partnership shows assets of £220,000 and liabilities of £45,000. At that date the partnership is dissolved and £325,000 is received for the assets, whereas the creditors for the liabilities settle for £42,000. What is the profit/(loss) on realisation?

(a) Profit of £108,000

(b) Loss of £108,000

(c) Profit of £105,000

(d) Loss of £105,000

4.6 Tom, Ben and Sarah are in partnership sharing profits and losses in the ratio of 2:2:1 respectively. Their balance sheet shows assets of £94,000 and liabilities of £36,000. At that date the partnership is dissolved and the assets realise £72,000 and the creditors for the liabilities receive £34,000. What is Sarah's share of any profit/loss on realisation?

(a) Profit of £4,800

(b) Loss of £4,800

(c) Profit of £4,000

(d) Loss of £4,000

4.7 Explain the accounting procedures that must be undertaken in order to admit a new partner to the business, where a revaluation of fixed assets takes place and where goodwill is valued and then eliminated from the books of account.

4.8 Outline the confidentiality procedures relating to changes in partners.

4.9 Bob, Roger and Graham who traded separately for several years decided to form a partnership on 1 April 20-1 and transferred all the assets and liabilities of their individual businesses to the partnership at that date.

Whilst the assets and liabilities brought into the partnership have been recorded in the partnership books of account at agreed valuations, it has now been discovered that recognition has not been given in the partnership books for the goodwill, as at 1 April 20-1, of the sole trader businesses transferred to the partnership ie:

	£
Bob	8,000
Roger	12,000
Graham	16,000

At the same time, it must be noted that the partners do not want a goodwill account to be maintained in the partnership books.

The partnership agreement provides for partners to be credited with interest on their capital account based on their year-end balances at the rate of 10% per annum. Roger and Graham are to be credited with partners' salaries of £10,000 and £13,000 per annum respectively and the balance of profits and losses to be shared between Bob, Roger and Graham in the ratio 5:3:2 respectively.

The following trial balance as at 31 March 20-2 has been extracted from the partnership accounts:

		£	£
Freehold premises:	at valuation	50,000	
	provision for depreciation		1,250
Plant & machinery:	at valuation	21,000	
	provision for depreciation		2,100
Motor vehicles:	at valuation	12,000	
	provision for depreciation		3,000
Stock		9,000	
Debtors		4,000	
Balance at bank		600	
Creditors			5,250
Capital accounts:	Bob		40,000
	Roger		20,000
	Graham		14,000
Drawings:	Bob	13,000	
	Roger	11,000	
	Graham	9,000	
Net profit for the year ended 31 March 20-2			44,000
		£129,600	£129,600

Additional information

It is agreed that a current account should be opened for each business partner.

REQUIRED

Task 1
Prepare the partners' capital accounts, showing the changes which should have taken place on the 1st April 20-1 for the introduction and elimination of goodwill.

Task 2
Prepare the partnership's profit and loss appropriation account for the year ended 31 March 20-2.

Task 3
Prepare the partnership's balance sheet as at 31 March 20-2.

4.10 The following is the summarised balance sheet of Ashley, Basil, Colin and Denzil who share profits and losses in the ratio of 4:3:2:1 respectively.

FIXED ASSETS	£	£
Premises	100,000	
Plant and Equipment	30,000	
Motor Vehicles	20,000	150,000
CURRENT ASSETS		
Stock	25,000	
Debtors	20,000	
Cash at bank	5,000	
	50,000	
CURRENT LIABILITIES		
Creditors	(25,000)	
NET CURRENT ASSETS		25,000
		175,000
Represented by:		
CAPITAL ACCOUNTS		
Ashley	60,000	
Basil	50,000	
Colin	40,000	
Denzil	25,000	175,000

The partners decide to dissolve the business, given the following proceeds of sale:

The premises when sold realised £160,000 whereas the plant and equipment was sold at auction for £26,000. The business vehicles were sold to a garage for cash totalling £18,000. The stock and debtors collectively realised £38,000 whereas the creditors after settlement discounts settled for £23,000. The costs of realisation and the auction amounted to £4,000 which was paid for by cheque.

REQUIRED

Draft the closing entries into the partnership books of account.

4.11 You have been asked by Middlemarch and Co, a partnership, to attend a meeting of the partners at which they will agree the year-end accounts. The partnership has a book-keeper who has kept the books and produced a profit and loss account for the partnership, but he requires some assistance to produce the final financial statements for the year ended 31 March 20-4. You have had a preliminary meeting with the book-keeper and have made notes of the information given as follows:

(a) The original partners of Middlemarch and Co were Brooke, Featherstone and Lydgate. They shared profits and losses in the following proportions: Brooke five-tenths, Featherstone three-tenths and Lydgate two-tenths.

(b) On 1 April 20-3, Mary Garth was admitted to the partnership. She agreed to introduce £8,000 in cash into the business. It was agreed that the new profit-sharing ratios were to be as follows:

Brooke	four-tenths
Featherstone	three-tenths
Lydgate	two-tenths
Garth	one-tenth

(c) At 1 April 20-3, goodwill was valued at £30,000. No account for goodwill is to be maintained in the books of the partnership, but adjusting entries in respect of goodwill are to be made in the capital accounts of the partners.

(d) Mary Garth is to receive a salary of £6,000. Lydgate already receives a salary of £5,000 and this is to be continued.

(e) Partners are to receive interest on their capital accounts of 10 per cent per annum on the balance outstanding at the end of the year. No interest is to be allowed on the balances of current accounts.

(f) The balances on the capital and current accounts at 1 April 20-3 were as follows:

	Capital	Current	
	£	£	
Brooke	20,000	4,500	CR
Featherstone	14,000	3,800	CR
Lydgate	9.000	1,800	DR

(g) In addition to her balance on the capital account, Brooke has loaned the partnership £8,000. She is entitled to interest on this loan at a rate of 8 per cent per annum.

(h) The partners' drawings during the year were as follows.

	£
Brooke	19,320
Featherstone	16,100
Lydgate	14,300
Garth	13,600

(i)   The net profit for the year to 31 March 20-4 as calculated by the book-keeper before taking into account partners' salaries and interest due was £56,740.

REQUIRED

Task 1

Prepare the partners' capital accounts for the year ended 31 March 20-4, accounting for the introduction of Mary Garth into the partnership.

Task 2

Draw up the appropriation account for the partnership of Middlemarch and Co for the year ended 31 March 20-4.

Task 3

Prepare the partners' current accounts for the year ended 31 March 20-4.

4.12 You have been approached by a partnership, Alice, Bonny and Clyde, to prepare their accounts for the year ending 31 October 20-4. You have established that profit available for appropriation is £78,000 for the year and have been given the following information.

(a)   Originally only Alice and Bonny were in partnership, sharing profits in a ratio of 2:1. On 1 November 20-3 they admitted the third partner, Clyde. Clyde contributed capital of £10,000 on 1 November 20-3. The new profit sharing ratio is 3:2:1 to Alice, Bonny and Clyde respectively.

(b)   Goodwill was valued at £30,000 on 1 November 20-3 and this must be taken into account when admitting Clyde; goodwill is not to be kept in the accounts. The profit sharing ratio to be used on elimination of the goodwill is 3:2:1 to Alice, Bonny and Clyde respectively.

(c)   Interest on capital is paid at a rate of 10 per cent based on the year-end capital amount. No interest is allowed on the balance of current accounts.

(d)   Drawings made for the year ending 31 October 20-4 were:

	£
Alice	38,000
Bonny	19,500
Clyde	15,000

(e)   Alice is entitled to a salary of £10,000 per annum, and Clyde is entitled to £5,000 per annum.

(f)   You have been supplied with the balance sheet of the partnership as at 31 October 20-3 (shown on the following page).

BALANCE SHEET OF ALICE AND BONNY AS AT 31 OCTOBER 20-3

	£	£
Fixed assets		
Vehicles	20,000	
Fixtures and fittings	4,000	
		24,000
Current assets		
Stock	8,000	
Debtors	3,500	
	11,500	
Current liabilities		
Creditors	2,000	
Bank overdraft	3,000	
	5,000	
Net current assets		6,500
Total assets less current liabilities		30,500
Represented by:		
Capital accounts		
Alice	14,000	
Bonny	10,000	
		24,000
Current accounts		
Alice	4,000	
Bonny	2,500	
		6,500
		30,500

REQUIRED

Task 1

Prepare the capital accounts of Alice, Bonny and Clyde for the year ended 31 October 20-4, showing clearly the effect of admitting Clyde to the partnership.

Task 2

Based on the above information, draw up an appropriation account for the partnership of Alice, Bonny and Clyde for the year ended 31 October 20-4.

Task 3

Prepare the partners' current accounts for the year ended 31 October 20-4.

5 INTRODUCTION TO LIMITED COMPANY ACCOUNTS

5.1 The abbreviation PLC stands for:

    (a)   Public limited company

    (b)   Private limited company

    (c)   Personal liability company

    (d)   Partners' liability clause

5.2 Any PLC in the UK must have a minimum authorised share capital of:

    (a)   £100,000

    (b)   £75,000

    (c)   £50,000

    (d)   £25,000

5.3 Which document issued by a limited company forms the constitution of the company, regulating its affairs to the outside world?

    (a)   Articles of Association

    (b)   Memorandum of Association

    (c)   Annual return

    (d)   Company prospectus

5.4 Reserves in a company belong to the:

    (a)   Ordinary shareholders

    (b)   Directors

    (c)   Debenture holders

    (d)   Creditors

5.5 Identify the advantages of forming a limited liability company over the creation of a partnership.

5.6 List the five main clauses of the Memorandum of Association.

5.7 Explain the difference between the nominal value and the market value of shares.

5.8 The following trial balance has been extracted from the books of account for Gooch PLC as at 31 May 20-5:

	Dr	Cr
	£000	£000
Administrative Expenses	210	
Distribution Costs	190	
Wages and Salaries	350	
Directors Fees	200	
Motor and Travel Costs	100	
Rent, Rates and Insurance	150	
General Expenses	120	
Called Up Share Capital		500
Debtors	500	
Cash at Bank and In Hand	50	
Share Premium Account		100
Land and Buildings:		
At Cost	1,000	
Accumulated depreciation (at 1 June 20-4)		100
Plant and Equipment:		
At Cost	800	
Accumulated depreciation (at 1 June 20-4)		320
Purchases	900	
Sales		2,500
Creditors		400
Stock (as at 1 June 20-4)	110	
Profit and Loss Account (at 1 June 20-4)		760
	4,680	4,680

Additional Information

Closing stock at 31 May 20-5 was valued at £130,000.

Corporation tax based on the company's profits for the year is estimated to be £80,000.

The company's authorised and Issued Share Capital consists of 1,000,000 Ordinary Shares of 50p each.

A final Ordinary Dividend of 10p per share is now proposed.

The company operates the following policy with regard to depreciation:

- Land and Buildings 2% per annum on cost

- Plant and Equipment 20% per annum on cost

REQUIRED

Task 1
Prepare the company's trading, profit and loss account for the year to 31 May 20-5.

Task 2
Prepare the company's balance sheet as at 31 May 20-5.

Task 3
Explain briefly how the balance on the share premium account arose.

Task 4
List three differences between ordinary shares and preference shares.

5.9   The following preliminary trial balance has been extracted from the books of Rafter plc for the year to 31 March 20-1.

	Dr	Cr
	£'000	£'000
Administrative expenses	1,300	
Advertising Expenses	10	
Authorised and issued share capital:		
ordinary shares of £1 each		500
8% preference shares of £1 each		500
Bad debt written off	500	
Cash at Bank	400	
15% Debentures		2,000
Debenture interest (to 30 September 20-0)	150	
Debtors and creditors	1,500	2,300
Share Premium Account		185
Directors' fees	350	
Distribution expenses	570	
Fixed assets: at cost	6,000	
accumulated depreciation (at 1 April 20-0)		800
General expenses	80	
Interim dividend (on ordinary shares, paid on 1 October 20-0)	40	
Purchases	5,600	
Profit and loss account (at 1 April 20-0)		435
Rent, rates, and insurance	630	
Sales		11,810
Stock (at 1 April 20-0)	1,400	
	18,530	18,530

Additional information

1   Stock at 31 March 20-1 was valued at £1,200,000.

2   The fixed assets are to be depreciated at a rate of 10% per annum on cost.

3   After the preparation of the above trial balance, it was discovered that £70,000 was owing for rent and rates, and £50,000 had been paid in advance for insurance.

4   The directors propose to pay a final ordinary dividend of 12p per share, and to pay all of the preference dividend due for the year.

5   Corporation tax payable on profits for the year to 31 March 20-1 is estimated to be £120,000.

6   The remaining debenture interest due in the year should now be accrued for.

REQUIRED

Prepare the company's profit and loss account for the year ended 31 March 20-1 and a balance sheet as at the same date.

5.10   The following draft trial balance has been extracted from the books of Squire plc as at 31 March 20-1.

	Dr.	Cr.
	£000	£000
Cash and bank	230	
Sales commission paid	6	
Interest paid	30	
Fixed assets at cost	1,100	
Fixed assets depreciation (at 1 April 20-0)		400
Office expenses	40	
Office rent, rates, heat and light	170	
Office wages and salaries	450	
Profit and loss account (at 1 April 20-0)		208
Purchases	1,200	
Sales		2,800
Share capital (ordinary shares of £1 each)		1,500
Stock at 1 April 20-0	200	
Trade debtors	1,280	
Trade creditors		178
Vehicle delivery expenses	320	
Communication expenses	60	
	5,086	5,086

Additional information:

The following items have not been taken into account in preparing the above trial balance:

1   Stock at 31 March 20-1 ws valued at £250,000.

2   Rates paid in advance at 31 March 20-1 amounted to £5,000.

3   Rent due at 31 March 20-1 amounted to £15,000.

4   Corporation tax based on the profits for the year is estimated at £120,000.

5   The company proposes to pay an ordinary dividend of 10p per share.

6   Depreciation is charged on the fixed assets at a rate of 20% on cost (on the assumption that there is no residual value) using the straight line method.

REQUIRED

Prepare the company's profit and loss account for the year ended 31 March 20-1 and a balance sheet as at the same date.

5.11   The following information relates to Placate PLC a company which buys and sells electrical goods.

The company's year end is the 30 June each year, and the Assistant Accountant has provided you with some draft accounts on an extended trial balance (see next page).

The following information has just come to light in order to complete the accounts:

1   Corporation tax due on this years profit is estimated to be £8,430.

2   The company's authorised and issued share capital is made up of 600,000 ordinary shares of 50p denomination. The directors have now decided to propose a final ordinary dividend of 5p per share.

REQUIRED

Task 1

Prepare journal entries as a result of the further information given above. Dates and narratives are not required.

Task 2

Prepare the company's profit and loss account for the year ended 30 June 20-6 and a balance sheet as at the same date.

Task 3

What are the main differences between a capital reserve and a revenue reserve on a limited company balance sheet?

EXTENDED TRIAL BALANCE

name: Placate PLC   date: 30 June 20-6

Description	Trial balance Dr £	Trial balance Cr £	Adjustments Dr £	Adjustments Cr £	Profit and loss Dr £	Profit and loss Cr £	Balance sheet Dr £	Balance sheet Cr £
Sales turnover		425,000				425,000		
Purchases	207,500				207,500			
Salaries & Wages	15,000		2,600		17,600			
Motor Expenses	13,500				13,500			
Rates	10,100			1,100	9,000			
Light and Heat	6,950		350		7,300			
Cleaning and Maintenance costs	4,250				4,250			
Advertising	3,600				3,600			
Stock	21,500		26,000	26,000	21,500	26,000	26,000	
Trade Debtors	20,500						20,500	
Provision for Doubtful Debts		3,160	1,110					2,050
Decrease in Provision for Doubtful Debts				1,110		1,110		
Cash in Hand	1,000						1,000	
Cash in Bank	6,500						6,500	
Trade Creditors		43,500						43,500
Bank Loan		50,000						50,000
Buildings (Cost)	515,000						515,000	
Fixtures and Fittings (Cost)	25,000						25,000	
Motor Vehicles (Cost)	80,000						80,000	
Share Premium Account		26,500						26,500
Buildings Accumulated Depreciation		50,000		25,750				75,750
Fixtures & Fittings Accumulated Depreciation		7,500		5,000				12,500
Motor Vehicles Accumulated Depreciation		40,000		20,000				60,000
Profit and Loss Account b/f		100,500						100,500
Depreciation - Buildings			25,750		25,750			
Depreciation - Fixtures & Fittings			5,000		5,000			
Depreciation - Motor Vehicles			20,000		20,000			
Interim dividend paid 1.1.20-6	30,000				30,000			
Returns Inwards	4,500				4,500			
Directors salaries	60,000				60,000			
Returns Outwards		6,900				6,900		
General Expenses	9,650				9,650			
Insurance	12,250			2,250	10,000			
Loan interest payable	6,260				6,260			
Accruals				2,950				2,950
Prepayments			3,350				3,350	
Capital		300,000						300,000
Profit / (loss) for the year					3,600			3,600
	1,053,060	1,053,060	84,160	84,160	459,010	459,010	677,350	677,350

6 PUBLISHED ACCOUNTS OF LIMITED COMPANIES

6.1 Which of the following expenses will not be analysed to distribution costs in a published profit and loss account for a limited liability company?

(a) Sales Director's remuneration

(b) Auditors fees

(c) Commission on sales

(d) Advertising costs

6.2 Which of the following expenses will not be analysed to administrative expenses in a published profit and loss account for a limited liability company?

(a) Bank charges and interest

(b) Office expenses

(c) General expenses

(d) Managing Director's salary

6.3 Which of the following fixed assets is not an intangible fixed asset?

(a) Goodwill

(b) Development costs

(c) Patents

(d) Plant and equipment

6.4 Which of the following does not appear under the heading 'Capital and reserves' in a published limited company balance sheet?

(a) Ordinary share capital

(b) Debentures

(c) Share premium account

(d) Preference shares

6.5 Which of the following does not normally appear under the heading 'Creditors, amounts falling due within one year'?

(a) Trade creditors

(b) Corporation tax payable

(c) Debentures

(d) Dividends proposed

6.6 Discuss the main differences between an exceptional item and an extraordinary item on a published limited company profit and loss account.

6.7 Identify four items for the notes to accounts which need to be reported upon according to the Companies Act 1985.

6.8 The Companies Act allows small and medium-sized private limited companies to file modified accounts with the Registrar of Companies. What are the criteria which warrants small and medium-sized status?

6.9 Hawksley plc is a trading company. The following information has been extracted from the books of account for the year to 31 March 20-2

	£'000
Auditors' remuneration	30
Corporation tax: based on the accounting profit for the year to 31 March 20-2	1,700
Delivery expenses	1,170
Dividends: final (proposed - to be paid 1 August 20-2)	2,000
interim (paid on 1 October 20-1)	500
Fixed assets at cost:	
Delivery vans	200
Office cars	40
Showroom Premises and equipment	5,000
Long term Bank Loan account	1,200
Office expenses	800
Office rent, rates, heat and light	350
Purchases	24,000
Sales	35,000
Stocks at cost:	
at 1 April 20-1	5,000
at 31 March 20-2	6,000
Showroom costs	1,000
Wages and salaries:	
Delivery staff	700
Directors' emoluments	300
Office staff	100
Showroom staff	400
Bank charges payable	125

Additional information

1   *Depreciation policy*

Depreciation is provided at the following annual rates on a straight line basis: delivery vans 20%; office cars 25%; showroom premises and equipment 10%.

2   The Directors' emolument can be split as follows:

	£000
Managing Director	120
Chairman	50
Marketing and Sales Director	60
Finance Director	70

3   There were 1,000,000 ordinary shares of £1 each in issue during the year to 31 March 20-2. There were no preference shares in issue.

REQUIRED

Using this information, prepare Hawksley plc's published profit and loss account for the year to 31 March 20-2 in accordance with the minimum requirements of the Companies Act 1985, and FRS3 (revised).

Note: a published balance sheet is not required for this activity.

6.10   The following preliminary trial balance has been extracted from the books of Davidson PLC for the year ended 31 March 20-1.

	Dr £'000	Cr £'000
Administrative expenses	800	
Advertising Expenses	50	
Authorised and issued share capital:		
ordinary shares of £1 each		800
10% Preference shares of £1 each		700
Bad debt	20	
Cash at Bank	35	
10% Debentures		1,000
Debenture interest (to 30 September 20-0)	50	
Debtors and creditors	1,345	600
Share Premium Account		250
Directors' fees	400	
Distribution expenses	355	
Fixed assets: at cost	2,500	
accumulated depreciation (at 1 April 20-0)		500
General expenses	60	
Interim dividend (on ordinary shares, paid on 1 October 20-0)	80	
Purchases	4,800	
Profit and loss account (at 1 April 20-0)		1,330
Rent, rates, and insurance	450	
Sales		8,500
Sales commission paid	60	
Wages and Salaries paid:		
Sales staff	190	
Distribution staff	285	
Stock (at 1 April 20-0)	2,200	
	13,680	13,680

Additional information

1   Stock at 31 March 20-1 was valued at £2,250,000.

2   The fixed assets are to be depreciated at a rate of 20% per annum on cost. The annual depreciation charge is apportioned 75% to administration and 25% to distribution.

3   After the preparation of the above trial balance, it was discovered that £50,000 was owing for rent and rates, and £100,000 had been paid in advance for insurance. Rent, rates and insurance are apportioned equally between administration and distribution expenses.

4   The directors propose to pay a final ordinary dividend of 20p per share, and to pay all of the preference dividend.

5   Corporation tax payable on profits for the year to 31 March 20-1 is estimated to be £140,000.

6   The Directors fees can be split as follows

	£000
Chairman	80
Managing Director	105
Finance Director	75
Marketing Director	70
Production Director	70

7   The remaining debenture interest due in the year should now be accrued for.

REQUIRED

From the information given prepare Davidson PLC's profit and loss account for the year ending 31 March 20-1 and a balance sheet as at that date in accordance with the minimum requirements of the Companies Act 1985, and FRS3 (revised).

6.11   The following information has been extracted from the books of Quest public limited company as at 30 September 20-7

	Dr. £'000	Cr. £'000
General Expenses	20	
Bank overdraft		2,400
Called up share capital (ordinary shares of £1 each)		4,000
Share Premium Account		200
Delivery expenses	2,800	
Fixed assets: at cost	3,500	
Fixed assets: accumulated depreciation (at 1 October 20-6)		1,100
Fixed asset investments	2,100	
Interest received		30
Interest payable	400	
Interim dividend paid	80	
Office expenses	3,000	
Other creditors		100
Other debtors	150	

Profit and loss account (at 1 October 20-6)		840
Purchases	12,000	
Sales		21,000
Stock (at 1 October 20-6)	500	
Trade creditors		180
Trade debtors	5,300	
	£29,850	£29,850

Additional information

The following additional information is to be taken into account:

1   Stocks at 30 September 20-7 were valued at £400,000.

2   At 30 September 20-7, £130,000 was outstanding for office expenses, and £50,000 had been paid in advance for delivery van licences.

3   Depreciation at a rate of 50% is to be charged on the historic cost of the tangible fixed assets using the straight line method; it is to be apportioned as follows:

	%
Cost of Sales	60
Distribution	30
Administration	10
	100

4   The corporation tax payable based on the profits for the year to 30 September 20-7 has been estimated at £80,000.

5   The directors propose to pay a final ordinary dividend of 3p per share.

REQUIRED

Task 1

Prepare journal entries for items 1-5 listed above. Dates and narratives are not required.

Task 2

In so far as the information permits, prepare Quest plc's profit and loss account for the year ending 30 September 20-7, and a balance sheet as at that date in accordance with the minimum requirements of the Companies Act 1985, and FRS3 (revised).

6.12   Woodpecker Ltd, a wholesale builders' merchant has asked the firm of accountants in which you work to provide assistance in drafting the financial statements of the company for the year ended 31 March 20-4. Woodpecker Ltd's financial accountant (who has left the company) produced an extended trial balance, which includes some of the normal year end adjustments, and gathered some further information which may be relevant to the year end accounts. You have been asked by one of the partners of your firm to take on the task.

The extended trial balance of Woodpecker Ltd is shown on the next page.

EXTENDED TRIAL BALANCE name: Woodpecker Limited date: 31 March 20-4

Description	Ledger balances Dr £000	Ledger balances Cr £000	Adjustments Dr £000	Adjustments Cr £000	Profit and loss Dr £000	Profit and loss Cr £000	Balance sheet Dr £000	Balance sheet Cr £000
Salaries and wages	1,468				1,468			
Salesmen's commission	102		4		106			
Motor expenses	72		6		78			
Sales		8,086				8,086		
Buildings (acc. dep.)		117		21				138
Fixtures and fittings (acc. dep.)		176		65				241
Motor vehicles (acc. dep.)		219		189				408
Office equipment (acc. dep.)		51		37				88
Investment revaluation reserve		150						150
Directors' pension contributions	15				15			
Advertising	67			11	56			
Stock	731		937	937	731	937	937	
Trade debtors	840						840	
Provision for doubtful debts		20		17				37
Goodwill	20						20	
Purchases	5,035				5,035			
Land and buildings (cost)	1,267						1,267	
Fixtures and fittings (cost)	632						632	
Motor vehicles (cost)	745						745	
Office equipment (cost)	194						194	
Investment property	800						800	
Depreciation (motor vehicles)			189		189			
Depreciation (fixtures and fittings)			65		65			
Depreciation (office equipment)			37		37			
Depreciation (buildings)			21		21			
Ordinary share capital		1,000						1,000
10 per cent Preference share capital		300						300
Directors' fees	7				7			
Share premium		250						250
Light and heat	19		7		26			
Interim dividend	15				15			
Increase in provision for doubtful debt			17		17			
General expenses	227		28		255			
Insurance	45			28	17			
Profit and loss account		778						778
Accruals				45				45
Prepayments			39				39	
Cash in hand	3						3	
Bank		139						139
Trade creditors		568						568
8 per cent Debentures		450						450
Profit					885			885
	12,304	12,304	1,350	1,350	9,023	9,023	5,477	5,477

The following further information is provided

1   The authorised share capital of the company is as follows:

4,000,000 ordinary shares of 25p each

500,000 10 per cent preference shares of £1.00 each

At the beginning of the year 1,600,000 shares were in issue (all were fully paid). A further 800,000 shares were issued during the year at a price of 75p per share. The whole of the proceeds of the issue, which were received in full, was credited to the ordinary share capital account.

2   The directors decided that instead of paying a dividend to ordinary shareholders they would make a bonus issue of shares at the year end. Ordinary shareholders received one ordinary share of 25p for every six ordinary shares held by them at the year end. No entries have been made in the extended trial balance to reflect this issue.

3   The interim dividend in the trial balance represents a dividend paid to preference shareholders. It has been decided to provide for the full preference dividend in the year end accounts but no entry has yet been made to reflect this decision.

4   No interest on the debentures has been paid during the year or provided for in the extended trial balance.

5   The investment property shown in the extended trial balance at a value of £800,000 represents an office building purchased by the company as an investment. It has been revalued by J Wheeler and Co, a firm of chartered surveyors, at £600,000 based on its value given its current use. The valuation has not been reflected in the extended trial balance.

6   Audit fees of £25,000 have not been paid or provided for in the extended trial balance.

7   The corporation tax charge for the year has been calculated as £275,000.

8   The balance on the goodwill account arose out of the purchase of an unincorporated business some years ago. The goodwill was purchased at a cost of £50,000 and is being amortised over ten years. No entry has been made for the amortisation of goodwill for the year ended 31 March 20-4.

9   The remuneration of the directors for the year was as follows:

	£
Chairman	31,000
Sales director	42,000
Executive director	56,000

The remuneration of the directors is included in the salaries and wages figure in the extended trial balance. The directors' fees and pension contributions made on behalf of the directors are made up as follows:

	Fees	*Pension contributions*
	£	£
Chairman	2,000	4,000
Sales director	2,000	5,000
Executive director	3,000	6,000
	7,000	15,000

The two directors, other than the sales director, work on general administration.

10   For the purposes of the published financial statements the following allocation of expenses is to be made:

	Distribution costs	Administrative expenses
	£000s	£000s
Motor expenses	47	31
Light and heat	20	6
Insurance	29	9
General expenses	186	48
Depreciation of motor vehicles	151	38
Depreciation of office equipment	22	15
Depreciation of buildings	16	5
Depreciation of fixtures and fittings	65	-

Salaries and wages, excluding directors' remuneration, are to be allocated on the basis of 75 per cent to the distribution department and 25 per cent to the administration department.

11   All of the operations of the company are continuing operations.

REQUIRED

Task 1

Make any adjustments you feel to be necessary to the balances in the extended trial balance as a result of the matters set out in the further information above. Set out your adjustments in the form of journal entries. (Ignore any effect of these adjustments on the tax charge for the year as given above).

Task 2

(a)   Draft a profit and loss account for the year ended 31 March 20-4 and a balance sheet as at that date in a form suitable for publication using Format 1 in accordance with the Companies Act 1985 as supplemented by FRS 3 'Reporting Financial Performance.' (Students are not required to prepare a statement of total recognised gains and losses or the reconciliation of movements in shareholders' funds required under FRS 3).

(b)   Provide suitable notes to the accounts, in so far as the information given above allows, for the following accounting items:

(i)   share capital

(ii)   directors' remuneration

6.13   You have just begun work as the assistant to the Financial Director of Tiny Toys Ltd, a company which buys and sells toys. Your predecessor prepared an extended trial balance for the year ending 31 December 20-3 prior to leaving. This includes the normal year-end adjustments. The Financial Director has asked you to review the trial balance in the light of some further information which may be relevant to the accounts. She has asked you to make any adjustments necessary before they are published.

The extended trial balance of Tiny Toys Ltd is shown opposite.

EXTENDED TRIAL BALANCE

name: Tiny Toys Limited   date: 31 December 20-3

Description	Ledger balances Dr £	Cr £	Adjustments Dr £	Cr £	Profit and loss Dr £	Cr £	Balance sheet Dr £	Cr £
Sales		183,500				183,500		
Purchases	114,300				114,300			
Carriage outwards	3,100				3,100			
Motor expenses	6,600		150		6,750			
Rates	3,900			330	3,570			
Advertising	2,200				2,200			
Salaries and wages	75,000				75,000			
Debtors	38,900						38,900	
Creditors		17,000						17,000
Cash in hand	500						500	
Cash at bank	4,000						4,000	
Stock	12,800		12,900	12,900	12,800	12,900	12,900	
Vehicles: cost	20,000						20,000	
depreciation		7,500		2,500				10,000
Office equipment: cost	4,000						4,000	
depreciation		1,000		500				1,500
Buildings: cost	40,000						40,000	
depreciation		8,000		4,000				12,000
General expenses	500				500			
Provision for doubtful debts		1,800		200				2,000
Increase in prov for doubtful debts			200		200			
Bad debt	1,000				1,000			
Depreciation: vehicles			2,500		2,500			
office equipment			500		500			
buildings			4,000		4,000			
Light and heat	1,700		150		1,850			
Loss						31,870	31,870	
Prepayment (rates)			330				330	
Accrual (light and heat)				150				150
Debentures		10,000						10,000
Share capital and reserves		94,700						94,700
Suspense		5,000		150				5,150
	328,500	328,500	20,730	20,730	228,270	228,270	152,500	152,500

The following further information is provided:

1 An audit fee of £950 needs to be provided for.

2 The amount representing share capital and reserves in the extended trial balance consists of 100,000 25p shares. The first issue of 50,000 shares was at par, a subsequent issue of 50,000 shares being at a premium of 30p and this balance remains in its entirety in the Share Premium Account. The remainder consists of the brought forward balance on the profit and loss reserve.

3 A decision has been made to use half of the Share Premium Account to make a bonus issue of ordinary 25p shares. No entries have been made in the extended trial balance to reflect this issue.

4 The amounts for rates and the depreciation of buildings should be split 50:50 between administrative and distribution cost classifications.

5 Included in the salaries are directors' emoluments of £45,000 of which £25,000 should be classed as administrative costs, the remainder being distribution costs. Also included in the salaries figure is £5,000 of the salesman's commission. The remainder of the salaries and wages should be split 60 per cent administration and 40 per cent distribution costs.

6 Eighty per cent of the depreciation charge for vehicles should be classified as a distribution cost, the remainder being an administrative cost. The office equipment depreciation should be classed as an administrative expense.

7 Of the light and heat costs, £1,000 should be classed as administrative costs, the remainder being distribution.

8 £6,000 of the total motor expense are distribution costs, the remainder being administrative.

9 General expenses should be classed as administrative expenditure.

10 A building costing £35,000, net book value £32,500 was sold for £37,500. The correct entries have been made in the buildings cost and depreciation accounts, as well as the bank account, but the profit figure does not appear to have been entered in the ETB profit and loss account.

11 On 1 December 20-3 there was an issue of 10,000 £1 nominal 12 per cent debentures at par. The issue has been correctly accounted for but no interest has been accrued.

12 The coding on the suspense account entry for £150 indicates it is an amount owing for motor expenses.

13 There is no tax charge for the year.

REQUIRED

Make any adjustments you feel necessary (in the form of journal entries) to the balances in the extended trial balance as a result of the matters set out in the further information. Draft a profit and loss account for the year ended 31 December 20-3 and a balance sheet as at that date.

6.14 You are employed by a firm of certified accountants and have been asked to prepare the financial statements of Franco Ltd (a company which distributes confectionery) for the year ending 31 March 20-5. A book-keeper at the company has prepared an extended trial balance for the year ending 31 March 20-5; this includes the normal year-end adjustments. You have been asked to review the trial balance in the light of some further information which may be relevant to the accounts and to make any adjustments necessary before they are published.

The extended trial balance of Franco Ltd is set out on the next page.

EXTENDED TRIAL BALANCE name: Franco Limited date: 31 March 20-5

Description	Ledger balances Dr £000	Ledger balances Cr £000	Adjustments Dr £000	Adjustments Cr £000	Profit and loss Dr £000	Profit and loss Cr £000	Balance sheet Dr £000	Balance sheet Cr £000
Turnover		2,470				2,470		
Purchases	1,000				1,000			
Salaries and wages	400				400			
Motor expenses	27				27			
Rates	25			5	20			
Light and heat	32		4		36			
Carriage inwards	14				14			
Advertising	95				95			
Stock	215		225	225	215	225	225	
Trade debtors	450						450	
Provision for doubtful debts		6		3				9
Increase in prov for doubtful debts			3		3			
Cash in hand	1						1	
Cash at bank	6						6	
Trade creditors		170						170
Land (cost)	375						375	
Buildings (cost)	200						200	
Fixtures and fittings (cost)	35						35	
Motor vehicles (cost)	94						94	
Office equipment (cost)	20						20	
Buildings (acc. dep.)		20		4				24
Fixtures and fittings (acc. dep.)		18		5				23
Motor vehicles (acc. dep.)		54		10				64
Office equipment (acc. dep.)		4		1				5
Depreciation - buildings			4		4			
Depreciation - fixtures and fittings			5		5			
Depreciation - motor vehicles			10		10			
Depreciation - office equipment			1		1			
Returns inwards	10				10			
Interim dividend	30				30			
Returns outwards		5				5		
General expenses	135				135			
Insurance	13			1	12			
Profit and loss account		160						160
Accruals				4				4
Prepayment			6				6	
Share capital - ordinary shares		200						200
- preference shares		50						50
Long term loan		20						20
Profit					683			683
	3,177	3,177	258	258	2,700	2,700	1,412	1,412

The following further information is provided:

1   The corporation tax charge for the year has been agreed at £110,000.

2   Motor expenses of £10,000 and wages of £2,000 have been wrongly included in the general expense figure in the trial balance. Of the remaining general expenses, £100,000 should be classified as administrative, the balance being distribution expenses.

3   The amount representing share capital and reserves in the extended trial balance consists of 400,000 50p ordinary shares and 50,000 £1 (8 per cent) preference shares. The directors have just declared the final dividend for the ordinary shares and this has not yet been entered into the accounts. The preference dividend also needs to be provided for. The total (ordinary and preference) dividend for the year amounts to £72,000.

4   Interest due on the long-term loan for the year needs to be provided for; it is charged at 10 per cent per annum.

5   An audit fee of £9,000 needs to be provided for.

6   Included in the total salaries figure is £98,000 of directors' emoluments. £68,000 of directors' emoluments should be classed as administrative expenses, the remainder being distribution. £104,000 of salaries and wages (excluding directors' emoluments) should be classed as administrative expenses, the remainder being distribution expenses.

7   Rates and light and heat should be split equally between administration and distribution expenses.

8   £27,000 of motor expenses are to be classed as distribution, the remainder as administration expenses.

9   The depreciation charges should be classed as:

	Administration	Distribution
	£	£
Buildings	3,000	1,000
Fixtures and fittings	4,000	1,000
Motor vehicles	2,000	8,000
Office	1,000	-

10   The insurance payment should be split in the ratio of 75/25 between administration and distribution expenses respectively.

REQUIRED

Task 1

Make any adjustments you feel necessary to the balances in the extended trial balance as a result of the matters set out in the further information above. Set out your adjustments in the form of journal entries. (Ignore any effect of these adjustments on the tax charge for the year).

Task 2

Draft a profit and loss account for the year ended 31 March 20-5 and a balance sheet as at that date in a form suitable for publication using Format 1 in accordance with the Companies Act as supplemented by FRS 3 'Reporting Financial Performance.' (You are NOT required to prepare a statement of total recognised gains and losses or the reconciliation of movements in shareholders' funds required under FRS 3). You should assume that all the information relates to continuing operations.

6.15 You have been asked to assist the directors of Lawnderer Ltd, a company that markets and distributes lawnmowers and other garden machinery, in the preparation of the financial statements for the year ended 30 September 20-5. The company employs a book-keeper who is competent in some areas of financial accounting but has gaps in his knowledge which you are required to fill. He has already prepared the extended trial balance which is shown on the next page.

The following further information is provided by the book-keeper:

1   The company disposed of motor vehicles during the year. The cost of the vehicles of £491,000 and the accumulated depreciation of £368,000 are still included in the figures in the trial balance. The sale proceeds of £187,000 were credited to the sales account.

2   Salesmen's commission of £52,000 relating to sales in the year has not been paid or charged as an expense in the figures in the trial balance.

3   Interest on the 9 per cent debentures has been included in the trial balance only for the first six months of the year.

4   The tax charge for the year has been calculated at £843,000.

5   A final dividend of 5 pence per share has yet to be provided for. The authorised and issued share capital of the company consists of shares with a nominal value of 25p.

6   Goodwill is being written off on a straight-line basis over a period of 10 years, but no amortisation has yet been charged in the trial balance.

7   The doubtful debts provision in the trial balance has not yet been adjusted for this year. The total doubtful debts provision required has been calculated at £115,000.

REQUIRED

Task 1

(a)   Make any adjustments you feel to be necessary to the balances in the extended trial balance as a result of the matters set out in the further information given by the book-keeper above. Set out your adjustments in the form of journal entries (narratives are not required).

(b)   Calculate the new retained profit which would result from these adjustments being made.

(Ignore any effect of these adjustments on the tax charge for the year as given above).

Task 2

Draft a balance sheet for the year ended 30 September 20-5, in a form suitable for publication, using Format 1 in accordance with the Companies Act 1985.

EXTENDED TRIAL BALANCE

name: Lawnderer Limited   date: 30 September 20-5

Description	Trial balance Dr £	Trial balance Cr £	Adjustments Dr £	Adjustments Cr £	Profit and loss Dr £	Profit and loss Cr £	Balance sheet Dr £	Balance sheet Cr £
Depreciation: Land and buildings			18		18			
Fixtures and fittings			72		72			
Motor vehicles			298		298			
Office equipment			24		24			
Goodwill	360						360	
Accruals				102				102
Dividends	120				120			
Interest on debentures	153				153			
Net sales		22,129				22,129		
Trade debtors	2,603						2,603	
Prepayments			43				43	
Bank overdraft		362						362
Cash in hand	3						3	
Purchases	14,112				14,112			
Stock 1.10.20-4	3,625				3,625			
Stock 30.9.20-5			4,572	4,572		4,572	4,572	
Profit and loss account 1.10.20-4	134						134	
Provision for doubtful debts		78						78
Trade creditors		2,967						2,967
Distribution costs	4,028		37	25	4,040			
9 per cent Debentures		3,400						3,400
Administration expenses	1,736		65	18	1,783			
Accumulated depreciation: Land and buildings		83		18				101
Fixtures and fittings		214		72				286
Motor vehicles		644		298				942
Office equipment		83		24				107
Land and buildings (cost)	1,875						1,875	
Fixtures and fittings (cost)	576						576	
Motor vehicles (cost)	1,691						1,691	
Office equipment (cost)	244						244	
Called up share capital		1,000						1,000
Share premium		300						300
Profit					2,456			2,456
	31,260	31,260	5,129	5,129	26,701	26,701	12,101	12,101

7 ACCOUNTING FOR ASSETS

7.1 Which of the following tangible fixed assets would not normally be depreciated?

(a) Leasehold buildings

(b) Freehold buildings

(c) Freehold land

(d) Revalued freehold buildings

7.2 According to SSAP 13 which of the following is not a criteria for capitalising development expenditure?

(a) Related expenditure is separately identifiable within the project

(b) The project has no specific aim or application

(c) The project is technically feasible

(d) The project is commercially viable

7.3 Which of the following situations qualify as an investment property according to SSAP 19?

(a) Property occupied by an unrelated third party

(b) Property owner occupied

(c) Property sublet to the parent company of a group

(d) Property sublet to a subsidiary company within the group

7.4 According to FRS 10, any purchased goodwill should be shown on the balance sheet as a:

(a) Fixed asset

(b) Current Asset

(c) Current liability

(d) Long term liability

7.5 Identify the main objectives of FRS 11 – Impairment of fixed assets and goodwill.

7.6 FRS 15 – Tangible fixed assets – stipulates that all tangible fixed assets should initially be recorded at cost. What constitutes 'cost' in these circumstances?

7.7 List the disclosure requirements in the published financial statements for government grants.

7.8 Explain the three most commonly used stock valuation methods.

7.9 Royal Berkeley PLC owns a large number of fixed assets throughout the UK, as part of its UK dealership. It now wants to standardise its procedures for depreciation in accordance with FRS 15.

Task 1

Define depreciation.

Task 2

Outline the policy decisions Royal Berkeley PLC has to consider when accounting for FRS 15 'Tangible fixed assets'.

7.10 SSAP 9 'Accounting for stock and long term work in progress' states that all stock should be valued at the lower of cost and net realisable value.

Outline what is meant by the term 'cost' and 'net realisable value'.

7.11 You have been asked to assist the directors of Lawnderer Limited, a company that markets and distributes lawnmowers and other garden machinery, in the preparation of the financial statements for the year ended 30 September 20-5.

The directors of the company have had a meeting with you regarding the possible treatment of certain future expenditure in the financial statements of the company. They have told you that the company has been approached by an inventor who has an idea to develop a revolutionary new lawnmower. The project looks technically feasible and preliminary marketing studies suggest a significant market for that product. Cost and revenue projections suggest that future profits should adequately cover the cost of development and have a beneficial effect on the future profitability of the company. The directors are concerned about the effect that the expenditure on developing the new product will have on future profits, given that it will take some time between commencing the project and commercial production.

Task

Explain how the costs of developing the new lawnmower would be reflected in the future financial statements of the company.

7.12 You have been approached by Samuel Taylor, a sole trader who runs a small trading company, Tayloriana (distributing catering equipment) for help in producing year-end financial statements. He employs a part-time book-keeper who has produced an extended trial balance for the business as at 31 March 20-5. Samuel is negotiating to enter into an existing partnership, Coleridge & Co, which operates in the same area of activity as his own. The existing partners of Coleridge & Co would like to see the latest profit figures of Samuel's business. You have been asked to assist in the preparation of a profit and loss account for the year ended 31 March 20-5.

Samuel Taylor has given you the following further information:

1   Stock has been counted on 31 March 20-5. The cost of the stock calculated on a first in first out basis is £49,300. The selling price of the stock is estimated at £65,450.

2   After the year-end, one of the debtors, whose year-end balance was £2,500 went into liquidation. The liquidator has stated that there will be no assets available to repay creditors. No provision for this bad debt has been made in the accounts and the balance is still included in year-end debtors.

Task

Explain to Samuel Taylor the appropriate accounting treatment of the above items by reference to applicable accounting standards.

7.13 Prepare briefing notes for a company Board meeting dealing with the following matters:

(a) How a balance could arise on a revaluation reserve.

(b) The recommendation of one of the directors is to lease assets as he says that this means that the assets can be kept off the balance sheet. Comment on this recommendation.

7.14 Elizabeth Ogier has asked you to assist in the preparation of the year end financial statements of her business. She operates a wholesale perfume business.

- The stock at the close of business on 30 September 20-9 was valued at cost at £49,477. However, included in this balance were some goods which had cost £8,200 but it is estimated that they could now be sold for only £4,800.

- The purchases figure includes goods to the value of £2,000 which Elizabeth took from the business for personal use and for gifts to friends.

Task

Draft a letter to Elizabeth justifying any adjustments you have made to:

- the stock valuation on 30 September 20-9

- the balances in the trial balance as a result of Elizabeth taking goods out of the business for her personal use or for gifts to friends

Your explanation should make reference, where relevant, to accounting concepts, accounting standards or generally accepted accounting principles.

8 ACCOUNTING FOR LIABILITIES AND PROFIT AND LOSS ACCOUNT

8.1 VAT is not reclaimable on certain business purchases. Which of the following purchases made by a VAT-registered business will include the VAT element as part of its overall cost?

(a) Purchase of plant and equipment

(b) Purchase of a car

(c) Purchase of a lorry

(d) Purchase of shop fittings

8.2 Corporation tax payable is included in a published balance sheet under:

(a) Provisions for liabilities and charges

(b) Deferred taxation

(c) Creditors, amounts falling due after more than one year

(d) Creditors, amounts falling due within one year

8.3 Payments on an operating lease will appear:

(a) In the profit and loss account as an expense

(b) In the balance sheet as a fixed asset

(c) In the balance sheet as a long term creditor

(d) In the profit and loss account as a non-trading revenue

8.4 According to FRS 12 – Provisions, contingent liabilities and contingent assets – which of the following words best describes a contingent liability?

(a) Probable

(b) Possible

(c) Remote

(d) Reliable

8.5 According to SSAP 17 – Accounting for post balance sheet events – something that exists after the balance sheet date but has no direct link with conditions that existed at the time of the balance sheet being drawn up is known as:

(a) An adjusting event

(b) A non-adjusting event

(c) A contingent liability

(d) A contingent asset

8.6   FRS 4 deals with Capital instruments. Explain the term 'capital instrument'.

8.7   FRS 12 deals with provisions, contingent liabilities and contingent assets. What is the difference between a provision and a contingent liability?

8.8   Explain what is demonstrated by a reconciliation of movement in shareholders' funds, according to FRS 3 – Reporting financial performance.

8.9   Discuss the difference between 'earnings per share' and 'dividend per share'.

8.10   According to FRS 8 – Related party disclosures – what are the circumstances in which related parties exist?

8.11   You have been asked by Eliot Productions Limited to attend a board meeting of the directors at which they will approve the year end accounts.

Task

Answer the following questions which the directors have asked about the year-end accounts. Justify your answers, where appropriate, by reference to accounting concepts, SSAPs and/or FRSs.

(a)   "We noted that, in preparing the accounts for the year, a debtor balance of £4,600 was written off as a bad debt, thus reducing profit by that amount. We understand that the debtor concerned had gone into liquidation after the year end and that we did not know that the debt would not be recoverable until after 31 March 20-4. Why did we not wait until next year to write off the debt since that is when the debtor went into liquidation?"

(b)   "The company is currently engaged in a legal case in which we are being sued for damages amounting to £53,000 arising out of a contract. Our lawyers claim that we have a very good defence to the claim and, in their opinion, it is unlikely that any damages will have to be paid. Can we ignore this claim for the purposes of our year-end financial statements?"

8.12   You are employed by a firm of certified accountants and have been asked to prepare the financial statements of Franco Ltd (a company which distributes confectionery) for the year ending 31 March 20-5.

Task 1

You have been asked by the directors of the company to prepare some briefing notes covering the following:

Stock is valued at the lower of cost and net realisable value in the accounts in accordance with the SSAP 9. The directors would like you to explain how cost and net realisable value are derived.

Task 2

The directors of Franco Ltd have drawn your attention to three matters and requested your advice on how these should be treated.

1   An issue of shares was made on 10 April 20-5. Fifty thousand ordinary shares of 50p each were issued at a premium of 25p.

2   A debtor owing £30,000 to Franco Limited on 31 March 20-5 went into liquidation on 3 April 20-5. The £30,000 is still unpaid and it is unclear whether any monies will be received.

3   The company is awaiting the outcome of a legal suit; an independent lawyer has assessed that it is probable that the company will gain £25,000 from it.

Write a memo to the directors of Franco Ltd outlining the required treatment for each of the three events.

8.13 Following your preparation of the balance sheet and profit and loss account of Deskover Ltd, you have had a meeting with the directors at which certain other matters were raised.

One of the debtors of Deskover Ltd has been having cashflow problems. The account balance at the end of the year was £186,000. Against this there was a specific provision of £93,000. One month after the year-end, the directors received a letter from the liquidators of the debtor stating that the business had gone into liquidation. The liquidators have stated that there will be no assets available to meet any of the debts of the unsecured creditors.

Task

State whether any adjustments need to be made to the financial statements of Deskover Ltd as a result of the liquidation of the debtor. Set out any adjustment required in the form of a journal entry and justify the accounting treatment by reference to applicable accounting standards.

9 CASH FLOW STATEMENTS

9.1 In a cash flow statement which one of the following would appear as an inflow of cash?
- (a) The profit on sale of a fixed asset
- (b) A repayment of debenture loans
- (c) An issue of shares at a premium
- (d) An increase in stock during the year

9.2 In a cash flow statement, which one of the following would appear as an outflow of cash?
- (a) An increase in debtors during the year
- (b) An increase in creditors during the year
- (c) Depreciation charges on fixed assets
- (d) Loss on sale of a fixed asset

9.3 In a cash flow statement, which one of the following is an operating activity?
- (a) An issue of shares
- (b) An issue of shares at a premium
- (c) The sale of some plant and equipment
- (d) A decrease in stock during the year

9.4 In a cash flow statement, which one of the following is a financing activity?
- (a) Interest payable and similar charges
- (b) Taxation paid
- (c) Equity dividends paid
- (d) Repayment of a long term loan

9.5 The operating profit of a business is £75,000; there were the following movements during the year:

Depreciation charges	£10,000
Increase in stock	£12,000
Decrease in debtors	£15,000
Decrease in creditors	£11,000

What is the net cash inflow from operating activities for the year?
- (a) £73,000 inflow
- (b) £123,000 inflow
- (c) £27,000 inflow
- (d) £77,000 inflow

9.6   In the reconciliation of operating activities, the profit on sale of tangible fixed assets is deducted because:

(a)   It is non-cash income

(b)   It is an investing activity

(c)   It is a financing activity

(d)   It is not part of a cash flow statement at all

9.7   List the eight main headings used in a cash flow statement.

9.8   Explain why revaluation surpluses do not appear in a cash flow statement.

9.9   Blackball PLC has made an operating profit of £121,000 during the year ending 31 August 20-4. The profit and loss account shows depreciation charges of £68,000 for the year and there was a profit on sale of plant and equipment amounting to £13,000. From the balance sheets for 20-4 and 20-3 the following extracted information is available:

	20-4	*20-3*
	£000	*£000*
CURRENT ASSETS		
Stock	29	35
Debtors	73	57
Cash at bank and in hand	14	7
	116	99
CURRENT LIABILITIES		
Trade Creditors	56	71
Corporation tax payable	23	37
Dividends proposed	19	25
	98	133

From the information provided, prepare a reconciliation statement between the cash flows from operating activities and operating profit for the year ending 31 August 20-4.

9.10 Set out below are financial statements for Underdesk Ltd for the year ending 20-7 and also for the previous year.

Underdesk Ltd
Profit and loss account for the year ended 31 December 20-7

	20-7 £000	20-6 £000
Turnover	5,490	4,573
Cost of sales	3,861	3,201
Gross profit	1,629	1,372
Depreciation	672	445
Other expenses	313	297
Profit on the sale of fixed assets	29	13
Operating profit for the year	673	643
Interest paid	156	47
Profit before tax	517	596
Taxation on profit	129	124
Profit after tax	388	472
Ordinary dividend	180	96
Retained profit	208	376

Underdesk Ltd
Balance sheet as at 31 December 20-7

	20-7 £000	20-7 £000	20-6 £000	20-6 £000
Fixed assets		5,461		2,979
Current assets				
Stock	607		543	
Debtors	481		426	
Cash			104	
	1,088		1,073	
Current liabilities				
Trade creditors	(371)		(340)	
Dividends payable	(180)		(96)	
Taxation	(129)		(124)	
Bank overdraft	(89)			
	(769)		(560)	
Net current assets		319		513
Long term loan		(1,700)		(520)
		4,080		2,972
Capital and reserves				
Called up share capital		1,400		800
Share premium		400		100
Profit and loss account		2,280		2,072
		4,080		2,972

Further information

Fixed assets costing £187,000 with accumulated depreciation of £102,000 were sold in 20-7 for £114,000. There were no other disposals in the year.

All sales and purchases were on credit. Other expenses were paid for in cash.

REQUIRED

Task 1

Provide a reconciliation between cash flows from operating activities and operating profit for the year ended 31 December 20-7 for Underdesk Ltd.

Task 2

Prepare a cashflow statement for Underdesk Ltd for the year ended 31 December 20-7 in accordance with the requirements of FRS 1.

9.11 The directors have provided you with the balance sheet of Games Ltd as at 30 September 20-8, along with some further information:

Games Ltd

Balance sheet as at 30 September 20-8

	20-8	20-7
	£000	£000
Fixed assets	1845	1615
Current assets		
Stocks	918	873
Trade debtors	751	607
Cash	23	87
	1,692	1,567
Current liabilities		
Trade creditors	583	512
Dividends payable	52	48
Taxation	62	54
	697	614
Net current assets	995	953
Long term loan	560	420
	2,280	2,148
Capital and reserves		
Called up share capital	1,000	1,000
Share premium	100	100
Profit and loss account	1,180	1,048
	2,280	2,148

Further information

- No fixed assets were sold during the year. The depreciation charge for the year amounted to £277,000.

- All sales and purchases were on credit. Other expenses were paid for in cash.

- The profit on ordinary activities before taxation was £246,000. Interest of £56,000 was charged in the year.

REQUIRED

Provide a reconciliation between cash flows from operating activities and operating profit for Games Ltd for the year ended 30 September 20-8.

Note:

You are not required to prepare a cash flow statement.

9.12 A colleague has asked you to take over the drafting of a cash flow statement for Diewelt Ltd for the year ended 30 September 20-9. Your colleague has already drafted a reconciliation between cash flows from operating activities and operating profit for the period. The financial statements of the company, drafted for internal purposes, along with the reconciliation are set out below with some further information relating to the reporting year:

Diewelt Ltd

Profit and loss account for the year ended 30 September 20-9

	20-9
	£000
Turnover	9,804
Cost of sales	5,784
Gross profit	4,020
Profit on sale of fixed asset	57
Depreciation	985
Other expenses	819
Operating profit for the year	2,273
Interest paid	365
Profit before tax	1,908
Taxation on profit	583
Profit after tax	1,325
Ordinary dividend	440
Retained profit	885

Diewelt Ltd

Balance sheet as at 30 September 20-9

	20-9 £000	20-9 £000	20-8 £000	20-8 £000
Fixed assets		6,490		5,620
Current assets				
Stocks	3,151		2,106	
Trade debtors	2,314		1,470	
Cash	103		383	
	5,568		3,959	
Current liabilities				
Trade creditors	964		1,034	
Dividends payable	264		192	
Taxation	583		491	
	1,811		1,717	
Net current assets		3,757		2,242
Long-term loan		(3,300)		(2,900)
		6,947		4,962
Capital and reserves				
Called up share capital		2,200		1,600
Share premium		800		300
Profit and loss account		3,947		3,062
		6,947		4,962

Further information

- A fixed asset which had cost £136,000 and had accumulated depreciation of £85,000 was sold during the year.

- All sales and purchases were on credit. Other expenses were paid for in cash.

Reconciliation of operating profit to net cash inflow from operating activities

	£000
Operating profit	2,273
Depreciation charges	985
Profit on sale of tangible fixed assets	(57)
Increase in stock	(1,045)
Increase in debtors	(844)
Decrease in creditors	(70)
Net cash inflow from operating activities	1,242

REQUIRED

Prepare a cash flow statement for Diewelt Ltd for the year ended 30 September 20-9 in accordance with the requirements of FRS 1.

9.13 Kasper PLC's profit and loss account for the year to 31 December 20-3 and balance sheets for 20-2 and 20-3 were as follows:

Kasper PLC Profit and Loss Account for the year to 31 December 20-3.

	£000	£000
Sales turnover		820
Materials	166	
Wages and salaries	98	
Depreciation charges	118	
Loss on disposal of fixed asset	18	400
Operating profit		420
Interest payable		30
Profit before tax		390
Taxation		130
Profit after tax		260
Dividends		64
Retained profit for the year		196

Kasper PLC Balance Sheets as at 31 December

	20-3		20-2	
	£000	£000	£000	£000
Fixed assets				
At cost	1,596		1,560	
Depreciation	318	1,278	224	1,336
Current assets				
Stock	24		20	
Debtors	66		50	
Cash at Bank	48		56	
Cash in Hand	10		8	
	148		134	
Current liabilities				
Creditors	12		6	
Taxation	102		86	
Dividends proposed	30		24	
	144		116	
Net current assets		4		18
		1,282		1,354
Long term liabilities				
Loans and debentures		200		500
		1,082		854
Capital and reserves				
Called up share capital		360		340
Share premium account		36		24
Profit and loss account		686		490
		1,082		854

Notes to the accounts

During the year the company paid £90,000 for a new piece of machinery

REQUIRED

Prepare a reconciliation statement for the cash flow from operating activities and operating profit for the year ended 31 December 20-3

Note: You are not required to prepare the actual cash flow statement.

9.14 Hill PLC's profit and loss account for the year to 31 December 20-3 and balance sheets for 20-2 and 20-3 were as follows:

Hill PLC abridged Profit and Loss Account for the year to 31 December 20-3.

	£
Operating profit	57,500
Interest receivable	2,500
Interest payable	(4,000)
Profit before tax	56,000
Taxation	(20,000)
Profit after tax	36,000
Dividends	(22,000)
Retained profit for the year	14,000

Hill PLC Balance sheets as at 31 December

	20-2		20-3	
FIXED ASSETS	£000	£000	£000	£000
Land & Buildings at cost	260		280	
Depreciation to date	(60)	200	(68)	212
Plant & Machinery at cost	164		200	
Depreciation to date	(54)	110	(86)	114
		310		326

CURRENT ASSETS

Stock	56		72	
Debtors	52		48	
Bank Deposit Account	16		20	
Cash in Hand/Bank	14		30	
	138		170	

CURRENT LIABILITIES

Creditors	40		54	
Taxation	32		24	
Dividends proposed	20		16	
	92		94	

NET CURRENT ASSETS		46		76
		356		402

LONG TERM LIABILITIES

20% Debentures		(80)		(20)
		276		382

CAPITAL AND RESERVES

Called up share capital		200		260
Share premium account		24		56
Profit and loss account		52		66
		276		382

Notes to the accounts

There were no sales of land and buildings during the year.

During the year the company sold plant costing £38,000 on which there was accumulated depreciation totalling £8,000. The net proceeds from the sale amounted to £24,000.

REQUIRED

Prepare a cash flow statement for Hill PLC for the year to 31 December 20-3 in accordance with FRS 1.

9.15 You have been asked to assist in the production of a reconciliation between cash flows from operating activities and operating profit for the year ended 31 July 20-6 for Poised Ltd. The financial statements of the company drafted for internal purposes are set out below, along with some further information relating to the reporting year.

Poised Ltd

Profit and loss account for the year ended 31 July 20-6

		20-6
		£000
Turnover		12,482
Opening stock	2,138	
Purchases	8,530	
Closing stock	(2,473)	
Cost of sales		8,195
Gross profit		4,287
Depreciation		1,347
Other expenses		841
Operating profit for the year		2,099
Interest paid		392
Profit before tax		1,707
Taxation on profit		562
Profit after tax		1,145
Ordinary dividend		360
Retained profit		785

Poised Ltd

Balance sheet as at 31 July 20-6

	20-6	20-5
	£000	£000
Fixed assets	6,867	6,739
Current assets:		
Stocks	2,473	2,138
Trade debtors	1,872	1,653
Cash	1,853	149
	6,198	3,940
Current liabilities:		
Trade creditors	1,579	1,238
Dividends payable	240	265
Taxation	562	477
	2,381	1,980
Net current assets	3,817	1,960
Long term loan	4,200	3,800
	6,484	4,899

Capital and reserves:

Called up share capital	3,000	2,500
Share premium	400	100
Profit and loss account	3,084	2,299
	6,484	4,899

Further information:

1   No fixed assets were sold during the year.

2   All sales and purchases were on credit. Other expenses were paid for in cash.

REQUIRED

Provide a reconciliation between cash flows from operating activities and operating profit for the year ended 31 July 20-6.

Note:

You are NOT required to prepare a cash flow statement.

10 INTERPRETATION OF FINANCIAL STATEMENTS

10.1 For the ratio Return on Capital Employed, which of the following best describes capital employed?

(a)   Share capital

(b)   Share capital + reserves

(c)   Share capital + reserves + long term liabilities

(d)   Share capital + reserves + long term liabilities + current liabilities

10.2 Which of the following formula best describes the acid test or quick ratio?

(a)   Current assets : Current liabilities

(b)   Debtors : Creditors

(c)   (Current assets – stock) : Current liabilities

(d)   Current assets : (Current liabilities – bank overdraft)

10.3 For the Asset Turnover ratio, which of the following best describes net assets?

(a)   Fixed Assets + Current assets

(b)   Fixed Assets + Current assets – Current liabilities

(c)   Current assets – Current liabilities

(d)   Fixed assets + Current assets – Current liabilities – Long term liabilities

10.4 The following information was extracted from the profit and loss account of Blue Dawn PLC for the year ending 31 December 20-7:

	£000
Operating profit	1,200
less Interest payable and similar charges	200
Profit before taxation	1,000
less Corporation Tax	150
Profit after taxation	850

What is the interest cover for the business?

(a)   8 times

(b)   6 times

(c)   5 times

(d)   1.2 times

10.5 The following information was extracted from the financial statements of Jacob PLC for the year 30 September 20-3

	£000
Sales	10,000
Purchases	4,000
Debtors	2,000
Creditors	1,000

What is the creditors payment period (to the nearest day)?

(a) 37 days

(b) 73 days

(c) 16 days

(d) 91 days

10.6 The following information was extracted from the balance sheet of Aktar PLC as at 31 July 20-5

	£000
15% Debentures	3,000
Ordinary shares of £1 each	5,000
10% Preference shares of 50p each	2,000
Share premium account	2,000
Profit and loss Account	8,000

What is the gearing ratio for the company?

(a) 20%

(b) 40%

(c) 25%

(d) 35%

10.7 Identify four user groups who would be interested in examining the financial ratios of a business.

10.8 Explain why the gearing and interest cover ratios are relevant to a investor who wishes to purchase ordinary shares in a company.

10.9 Jonathan Fisher is intending to invest a substantial sum of money in a company. A colleague has suggested to him that he might want to invest in a private company called Carp Ltd which supplies the pond equipment to retail outlets. You have been asked to assist him in interpreting the financial statements of the company which are set out below:

Carp Ltd

Summary Profit and Loss Account for the year ended 30 September 20-9

	20-9	20-8
	£000	£000
Turnover	3,183	2,756
Cost of sales	1,337	1,020
Gross profit	1,846	1,736
Expenses	1,178	1,047
Net profit before interest and tax	668	689
Interest	225	92
Profit before tax	443	597
Taxation	87	126
Profit after tax	356	471
Dividends	42	50
Retained profit	314	421

Carp Ltd

Summary balance sheets as at 30 September 20-9

	20-9		20-8	
	£000	£000	£000	£000
Fixed assets		4,214		2,030
Current assets				
Stock	795		689	
Debtors	531		459	
Cash	15		136	
	1,341		1,284	
Current liabilities				
Trade creditors	709		435	
Proposed dividend	42		50	
Taxation	87		126	
	838		611	
Net current assets		503		673
Long term loan		(2,500)		(1,000)
		2,217		1,703
Share capital		700		500
Profit and loss account		1,517		1,203
		2,217		1,703

REQUIRED

Prepare notes for Jonathan Fisher covering the following points:

1   Calculate the following ratios for the two years:
(a)   gearing
(b)   net profit percentage
(c)   current ratio
(d)   return on equity

2   Using the ratios calculated, comment on the company's profitability, liquidity and financial position and consider how these have changed over the two years.

3   Using only the calculation of the ratios and the analysis of the changes over the two years, state whether the company is a better prospect for investment in 20-9 than it was in 20-8. Give reasons for your answers.

10.10   A director of the company where you work is going to a conference where one of the topics to be discussed is gearing. He has asked you to prepare a briefing paper containing the following points:
•   What do you understand by the term gearing?
•   What effect can gearing have on a company's profit and how will gearing affect the overall return to the ordinary shareholder?
If possible you should supply a worked example to back up your answer.

10.11   Botticelli Ltd is a trading company that sells carpets to retail outlets. The shareholders of Botticelli Ltd have some questions about the profitability and liquidity of the company and about how cash flows from operating activities can be reconciled to operating profit. The profit and loss account and balance sheet produced for internal purposes are set out below:

Botticelli Ltd
Profit and loss account for the year ended 31 December 20-6

	20-6		20-5	
	£000	£000	£000	£000
Turnover		2,963		1,736
Opening stock	341		201	
Purchases	1,712		1,097	
Closing stock	(419)		(341)	
Cost of sales		1,634		957
Gross profit		1,329		779
Depreciation		247		103
Other expenses		588		334
Profit on the sale of fixed assets		15		-
Operating profit for the year		509		342
Interest paid		78		26
Profit before tax		431		316
Taxation on profit		138		111
Profit after tax		293		205
Ordinary dividend		48		22
Retained profit		245		183

Botticelli Ltd

Balance sheet as at 31 December 20-6

	20-6	20-5
	£000	£000
Fixed assets	2,800	1,013
Current assets:		
Stock	419	341
Debtors	444	381
Cash	–	202
	863	924
Current liabilities:		
Trade creditors	322	197
Dividends payable	48	41
Taxation	158	103
Bank overdraft	194	-
	722	341
Net current assets	141	583
Total assets less current liabilities	2,941	1,596
Long term loan	(970)	(320)
	1,971	1,276
Capital and reserves:		
Called up share capital	400	200
Share premium	250	-
Profit and loss account	1,321	1,076
	1,971	1,276

REQUIRED

Prepare a report to the shareholders about the profitability and liquidity of Botticelli Ltd for the two years 20-5 and 20-6. Your report should include:

(a)   calculation of the following ratios for the two years:

   – return on capital employed

   – gross profit ratio

   – net profit ratio

   – current ratio

   – quick ratio (also called acid test)

(b)   comments on the changes in the ratios from 20-5 to 20-6.

10.12 Due to the success of its board game 'The Absolute', McTaggart Ltd is thinking of expanding its operations. It has identified another company, Hegel Ltd, which also distributes board games, as a possible target for takeover. The directors have obtained a set of financial statements of the company for the last two years; these have been prepared for internal purposes. Hegel Ltd's year end is 30 September.

The directors have a number of questions relating to the company and to the possible takeover which they would like you to answer. The financial statements for Hegel Ltd are set out below:

Hegel Ltd

Profit and loss account for the year ended 30 September 20-7

	20-7		20-6	
	£000	£000	£000	£000
Turnover		6,995		3,853
Opening stock	681		432	
Purchases	4,245		2,561	
Closing stock	(729)		(681)	
Cost of sales		4,197		2,312
Gross profit		2,798		1,541
Depreciation		971		311
Other expenses		593		415
Profit on the sale of fixed assets		20		-
Operating profit for the year		1,254		815
Interest paid		302		28
Profit before tax		952		787
Taxation on profit		333		276
Profit after tax		619		511
Ordinary dividend		144		120
Retained profit		475		391

Hegel Ltd

Balance sheet as at 30 September 20-7

	20-7	20-6
	£000	£000
Fixed assets	6,472	2,075
Current assets:		
Stocks	729	681
Debtors	574	469
Cash	–	320
	1,303	1,470
Current liabilities:		
Trade creditors	340	424
Dividends payable	144	120
Taxation	333	276
Bank overdraft	158	–
	975	820
Net current assets	328	650
Long term loan	(3,350)	(350)
	3,450	2,375
Capital and reserves:		
Called up share capital	1,200	1,000
Share premium	400	–
Profit and loss account	1,850	1,375
	3,450	2,375

Further information

All sales and purchases were on credit. Other expenses were paid for in cash.

REQUIRED

Prepare a report for the directors of McTaggart Ltd which covers the relevant calculations and questions set out below:

(a) Calculate the current and quick ratios (also known as the 'acid test') of Hegel Ltd for the two years. Using this information state how the liquidity of Hegel Ltd has changed from 20-6 to 20-7.

(b) Calculate the gearing ratio for Hegel Ltd for 20-6 and 20-7 and comment on the results. Explain whether the level of borrowings in Hegel Ltd would have any impact on the level of gearing in the group accounts of McTaggart Ltd.

11 CONSOLIDATED ACCOUNTS

11.1 Active PLC invested £220,000 in 120,000 ordinary shares of 50 pence each of Doldrums PLC. The issued share capital and reserves of Doldrums PLC at the time of acquisition were £80,000 in shares and £60,000 in reserves (£140,000 in total).

What is the value of goodwill arising on acquisition?

(a)   £80,000

(b)   £115,000

(c)   £55,000

(d)   £140,000

11.2 The issued share capital of Sub Let PLC is 800,000 ordinary shares of 10 pence each. The reserves are: share premium account £40,000, revaluation reserve £25,000 and the profit and loss account £85,000. The parent company Ask Right PLC currently owns 500,000 of the ordinary shares in Sub Let PLC.

What is the total value for minority interest?

(a)   £86,250

(b)   £356,250

(c)   £300,000

(d)   £143,750

11.3 The balance sheet of Father PLC includes trade debtors of £65,000 and its subsidiary company Son Ltd has trade debtors totalling £32,000. The accounts also show trade creditors to be £52,000 and £18,000 respectively. However included in these amounts are inter group balances of £7,000 (Father PLC owes Son Ltd).

In the consolidated balance sheet of the group what will be the respective trade debtors and trade creditors figures?

(a)   £97,000 and £70,000

(b)   £104,000 and £77,000

(c)   £90,000 and £63,000

(d)   £33,000 and £34,000

11.4   Mother PLC acquires 80% of the ordinary shares in Daughter Ltd, on 1 April 20-7. The net profit after tax reported by Daughter Ltd for the year ending 31 March 20-8 amounted to £65,000.

What is the minority interest that would appear in the consolidated profit and loss account for the year ended 31 March 20-8?

(a)   £52,000

(b)   £65,000

(c)   £26,000

(d)   £13,000

11.5   Duck PLC owns 55% of the ordinary shares in Duckling Ltd. Sales for the year for Duck PLC amounted to £800,000 whereas Duckling Ltd grossed sales of £350,000. Duckling Ltd sales include goods sold to Duck PLC for £16,000. These goods as yet have not been resold by Duck PLC to any customer.

What is the correct value for sales which will appear in the consolidated profit and loss account?

(a)   £1,150,000

(b)   £992,500

(c)   £1,118,000

(d)   £1,134,000

11.6   What is the correct term used for a subsidiary company's reserves at the time of acquisition by a parent company?

(a)   Pre-acquisition profit

(b)   Post-acquisition profit

(c)   Takeover profit

(d)   Minority interest

11.7   FRS 2 – Accounting for subsidiary undertakings – uses the terms 'dominant influence' and 'participating interest'. Explain the meaning of these terms.

11.8   Identify the principal differences between the acquisition method and the merger method, when preparing consolidated accounts.

11.9   Explain the guidance given by FRS 7 – Fair values in acquisition accounting – for the valuation of assets in a set of consolidated accounts.

11.10 An investment figure of £4,010,000 shown in the financial statements of Deskover Ltd represents the cost of acquiring shares in a subsidiary undertaking, Underdesk Ltd. Deskover Ltd acquired 75% of the ordinary share capital of Underdesk Ltd on 31 December 20-7. The directors have obtained a balance sheet of the company for the last two years, prepared for internal purposes. Underdesk Ltd's year end is also 31 December. The net assets of Underdesk Ltd are shown in the balance sheet at their fair values except for the fixed assets, which have a fair value at 31 December 20-7 of £5,761,000.

Underdesk Ltd

Balance sheet as at 31 December 20-7

	20-7		20-6	
	£000	£000	£000	£000
Fixed assets		5,461		2,979
Current assets				
Stocks	607		543	
Debtors	481		426	
Cash			104	
	1,088		1,073	
Current liabilities				
Trade creditors	(371)		(340)	
Dividends payable	(180)		(96)	
Taxation	(129)		(124)	
Bank overdraft	(89)		–	
	(769)		(560)	
Net current assets		319		513
Long term loan		(1,700)		(520)
		4,080		2,972
Capital reserves				
Called up share capital		1,400		800
Share premium		400		100
Profit and loss account		2,280		2,072
		4,080		2,972

REQUIRED

Calculate the goodwill on consolidation that arose on acquisition of the shares in Underdesk Ltd on 31 December 20-7. Set out the possible accounting treatments of this goodwill in the group accounts of Deskover Ltd, justifying your answer by reference to applicable accounting standards.

Note:

You are not required to produce a consolidated balance sheet for the group.

11.11 The directors of Fun Ltd have a number of questions relating to the financial statements of their recently acquired subsidiary, Games Ltd. Fun Ltd acquired 75% of the ordinary share capital of Games Ltd on 30 September 20-8 for £2,244,000. The fair value of the fixed assets in Games Ltd as at 30 September 20-8 was £2,045,000. The directors have provided you with the balance sheet of Games Ltd as at 30 September 20-8 along with some further information:

Games Ltd

Balance sheet as at 30 September 20-8

	20-8	20-7
	£000	£000
Fixed assets	1,845	1,615
Current assets		
Stocks	918	873
Trade debtors	751	607
Cash	23	87
	1,692	1,567
Current liabilities		
Trade creditors	583	512
Dividends payable	52	48
Taxation	62	54
	697	614
Net current assets	995	953
Long term loan	560	420
	2,280	2,148
Capital and reserves		
Called up share capital	1,000	1,000
Share premium	100	100
Profit and loss account	1,180	1,048
	2,280	2,148

REQUIRED

Prepare notes to take to the Board meeting to answer the following questions of the directors:

(a)   What figure for the minority interest would appear in the consolidated balance sheet of Fun Ltd as at 30 September 20-8?

(b)   Where in the balance sheet would the minority interest be disclosed?

(c)   What is a 'minority interest'?

11.12 You have been asked to assist in the preparation of the consolidated accounts of the Shopan Group. Set out below are the balance sheets of Shopan Ltd and its subsidiary undertaking Hower Ltd, as at 30 September 20-9:

Balance sheets as at 30 September 20-9

	Shopan Ltd		Hower Ltd	
	£000	£000	£000	£000
Fixed assets		6,273		1,633
Investment in Hower Ltd		2,100		
Current assets				
Stocks	1,901		865	
Debtors	1,555		547	
Cash	184		104	
	3,640		1,516	
Current liabilities				
Trade creditors	1,516		457	
Taxation	431		188	
	1,947		645	
Net current assets		1,693		871
Long term loan		(2,870)		(400)
		7,196		2,104
Capital and reserves				
Called up share capital		2,000		500
Share premium		950		120
Profit and loss account		4,246		1,484
		7,196		2,104

Further information

- The share capital of both Shopan Ltd and Hower Ltd consists of ordinary shares of £1 each.
- Shopan Ltd acquired 375,000 shares in Hower Ltd on 30 September 20-9.
- The fair value of the fixed assets of Hower Ltd at 30 September 20-9 was £2,033,000.

REQUIRED

Task 1

Prepare the consolidated balance sheet for Shopan Ltd and its subsidiary undertaking as at 30 September 20-9.

Task 2

FRS 2 states that 'a parent undertaking should prepare consolidated financial statements for its group'. Give two of the criteria that according to FRS 2, determine whether an undertaking is the parent undertaking of another undertaking.

11.13 The Finance Director of Fairway plc has asked you to prepare the draft consolidated profit and loss account for the group. The company has one subsidiary, Green Limited. The profit and loss accounts of the two companies, prepared for internal purposes, for the year ended 30 June 20-2 are as follows:

	Fairway plc	Green Ltd
	£000	£000
Turnover	12,200	4,400
Cost of sales	8,500	3,100
Gross profit	3,700	1,300
Distribution costs	1,600	500
Administrative expenses	400	200
Dividends received from Green Ltd	80	–
Profit on ordinary activities before interest	1,780	600
Interest paid	300	200
Profit on ordinary activities before taxation	1,480	400
Tax on profit on ordinary activities	400	100
Profit on ordinary activities after taxation	1,080	300
Dividends	700	100
Retained profit for the financial year	380	200

Further information:

- Fairway plc acquired 80% of the ordinary share capital of Green Limited on 1 July 20-1.

- During the year Green Limited sold stock which had cost £750,000 to Fairway plc for £1,000,000. All the stock had been sold by Fairway plc by the end of the year.

- Ignore any write-off of goodwill for the period.

REQUIRED

Draft a consolidated profit and loss account for Fairway plc and its subsidiary undertaking for the year ended 30 June 20-2.

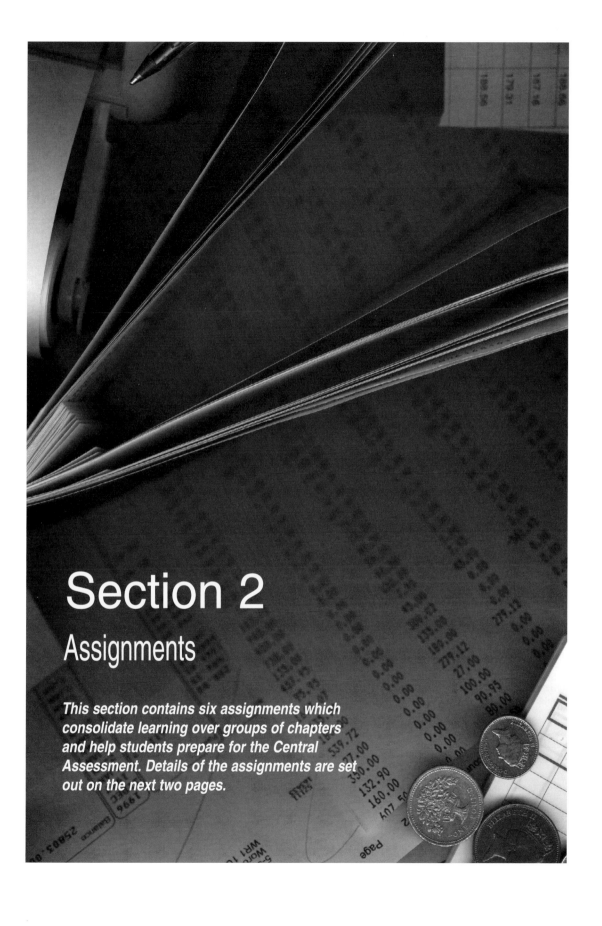

Section 2

Assignments

This section contains six assignments which consolidate learning over groups of chapters and help students prepare for the Central Assessment. Details of the assignments are set out on the next two pages.

INTRODUCTION TO ASSIGNMENTS

These Assignments are designed to be used for practice as you progress through the *Financial Statements Tutorial* text. It is important to be able to apply the appropriate methods and techniques that you have learned to whatever Case Study scenario you may be given.

These Assignments therefore provide a variety of situations. Most of them are linked to groups of two chapters of the tutorial. The last assignment concentrates on the topic of consolidated accounts. The list opposite shows the relevant chapters which should be studied before attempting each Assignment.

This section is not intended to give complete coverage of Unit 11 on its own. Further practice can be gained by using the chapter activities (Section 1) and the practice Central Assessments (Section 3).

Assignment	relevant Tutorial chapters	page
1 FINANCIAL STATEMENTS IN THE BOOK TRADE Financial statements & Sole Trader accounts	1,2	88
2 DEALING WITH PARTNERSHIP CLIENTS Partnership accounts	3,4	90
3 DRAFTING COMPANY ACCOUNTS Private and public limited company accounts	5,6	93
4 ADVISING ON ACCOUNTING POLICIES Accounting policies and accounting standards	7,8	99
5 CASH FLOW STATEMENTS AND RATIOS Preparing cash flow statements; calculating and commenting on accounting ratios	9,10	102
6 CONSOLIDATED ACCOUNTS Preparing consolidated accounts; dealing with associated companies and fair value	11	106

FINANCIAL STATEMENTS IN THE BOOK TRADE

1

SITUATION

You are an Accounts Assistant at Vision Press Limited, a publisher of childrens' books. You first qualified as an accountant but have worked for twenty years in the book trade in various financial roles and are often called upon to provide help and advice to start-up businesses.

TASKS

1 You attend a board meeting following the production of the draft financial statements of Vision Press by your accountants. You have to answer a number of questions asked by other directors who are less familiar with accounting concepts than you are. How would you answer these?

    (a) Why is stock shown on the company balance sheet as a current asset, when it is a permanent asset of the business? The company is very careful in that it offers a buffer stock system which means that it will never run out of stock completely. With this in mind wouldn't it make more sense to show stock as a fixed asset on the balance sheet?

    (b) Why are the business premises shown as a fixed asset when in fact they are a liability to the business as we owe the bank a substantial amount of money on those premises in the form of a commercial mortgage? This must be the case, because the mortgage is listed under the heading long-term liabilities in the balance sheet?

    (c) The employees' representatives in the form of their local trade union have requested a copy of the published accounts. Why would they want to see them?

2 A friend of yours, Danny Stevenson, has started a sole trader book wholesale business. He buys in bulk from book publishers and sells the books to the book trade. He has just produced his trial balance as at 31 December 20-5 and has made some notes about his accounts.

He seeks your advice and asks you as a favour to prepare his trading and profit and loss account for the year ended 31 December 20-5 and a balance sheet at that date.

Danny Stevenson
Trial balance as at 31 December 20-5

	Dr	Cr
	£	£
Property, at cost	120,000	
Equipment, at cost	80,000	
Provisions for depreciation (as at 1 January 20-5)		
- on property		20,000
- on equipment		38,000
Purchases	250,000	
Sales		402,200
Stock (as at 1 January 20-5)	50,000	
Discounts allowed	18,000	
Discounts received		4,800
Returns out		15,000
Wages and salaries	58,800	
Bad debts	4,600	
Loan interest	5,100	
Other operating expenses	17,700	
Trade creditors		36,000
Trade debtors	38,000	
Cash on hand	300	
Bank	1,300	
Drawings	24,000	
Provision for bad debts		500
17% long-term loan		30,000
Capital (as at 1 January 20-5)		121,300
	667,800	667,800

additional information

The following additional information as at 31 December 20-5 is available.

* Stock as at the close of business has been valued at cost at £42,000.

* Wages and salaries are accrued by £800.

* Other operating expenses are prepaid by £300.

* The provision for bad debts is to be adjusted so that it is 2% of trade debtors.

* Depreciation for the year ended 31 December 20-5 has still to be provided as follows:

    Property: 1.5% per annum using the straight-line method;

    Equipment: 2.5% per annum using the diminishing-balance method.

DEALING WITH PARTNERSHIP CLIENTS

SITUATION

You work for a firm of accountants, Gardner and Bellfield. You are the firm's expert in dealing with partnership businesses. During the course of a week you are given a number of assignments.

TASKS

1   You are required to attend a meeting of the partners Alice Grace, Ethel Grace and Isabella Grace. They are three sisters who are in partnership together selling gardening equipment. They share profits in the ratio:

Alice   5/12

Ethel   4/12

Isabella   3/12

They will admit a fourth partner, Flora Bundy into the business on 1 June 20-7. She will invest £30,000 into the partnership. The profit sharing ratios will then become:

Alice   4/10

Ethel   3/10

Isabella   2/10

Flora   1/10

You have been given the following additional information:

(1)   The business has freehold land and buildings which originally cost £120,000 and on which, at 31 May 20-7, there is accumulated depreciation of £25,000. The land and buildings have recently been revalued at £179,000.

(2)   Motor vehicles originally cost £24,000 and on 31 May 20-7 there is accumulated depreciation of £8,400. They are now thought to be worth only £6,000.

(3)   The new values of the freehold and buildings and the motor vehicles are to be incorporated into the partnership on admission of the new partner with any adjustment being made in the capital accounts of the partners.

(4)   Goodwill has been valued at £144,000 and it has been agreed to adjust the capital balances of the partners to reflect the goodwill that exists in the business. A goodwill account is to be maintained in the new partnership.

The capital account balances for the existing partnership at 31 May 20-7 are as follows:

Alice	£55,000
Ethel	£45,000
Isabella	£40,000

REQUIRED

(a)   Make the necessary entries in the capital accounts of the partners to reflect the admission of Flora into the partnership on 1 June 20-7, taking into account the terms of entry.

(b)   Draft notes to take to the meeting to explain why adjustments to the partners' capital accounts are necessary to take into account the new values of the land and buildings and the motor vehicles.

2   Sven, Ben and Len are in partnership, sharing profits and losses in the ratio 3:2:1 respectively. Ben is to retire on 31 August 20-7 and is to be paid the amount due to him by cheque from the business bank account.

The balance sheet drawn up immediately prior to Ben's retirement is as follows:

	£
Fixed Assets	40,000
Current Assets	12,000
Cash at bank	28,000
Current Liabilities	(20,000)
	60,000
Capital Accounts:	
Sven	28,000
Ben	18,000
Len	14,000
	60,000

Additional information

Goodwill is to be valued in the business immediately prior to Ben's departure at £30,000, but no goodwill is to remain in the books after Ben's retirement.

Fixed assets are to be revalued at £52,000 as at 31 August 20-7.

In the new partnership Sven and Len are to share profits and losses in the ratio 3:2 respectively.

REQUIRED

(a)   Complete the partners capital accounts, showing the amount to be paid to Ben upon his retirement.

(b)   Complete the balance sheet for Sven and Len as at 1 September 20-7.

(c)   Sven is worried about the need to create a new partnership agreement. Explain to the partners how the profits in a partnership are to be allocated if no partnership agreement exists.

(d)   List five items which can typically be found in a partnership agreement.

3   Maxwell, Silver and Hammer have been in partnership for a number of years. Recently they have been experiencing losses, and because of this they have decided to close down the partnership and cease trading as from 31 January 20-7.

The partnership balance sheet as at 31 January 20-7 prior to any sell off was as follows:

	£	£	£
Fixed Assets			
Land and Buildings		140,000	
Shop Equipment		65,000	
Delivery Vehicles		40,000	245,000
Current Assets			
Stock		65,000	
Debtors		32,000	
		97,000	
Current Liabilities			
Bank overdraft	33,000		
Creditors	60,000	93,000	
Net Current Assets			4,000
			249,000
Long Term Liabilities			
Loan Account – Silver			40,000
			209,000
Represented by:			
Capital Accounts			
Maxwell		70,000	
Silver		50,000	
Hammer		10,000	130,000
Current Accounts			
Maxwell		35,000	
Silver		45,000	
Hammer		(1,000)	79,000
			209,000

Maxwell, Silver and Hammer have always shared profits and losses on an equal basis. In the process of dissolution the assets were realised for the following cash amounts:

	£
Land and Buildings	150,000
Shop Equipment	30,000
Delivery Vehicles	25,000
Stock	50,000
Debtors	26,000
Total proceeds	281,000

The business creditors were fully settled by the partnership, with the creditors being paid in full £59,000. Silver has agreed to add the value of the loan to his capital account as part of his overall settlement.

REQUIRED

The partners want to know what each of them is to receive. Close off the books of account of the partnership, showing clearly the amounts receivable or payable in cash for each respective partner.

3

DRAFTING COMPANY ACCOUNTS

SITUATION

You work for a firm of accountants, Swinburn, Stanfield & Co. During the course of the week you have been given a number of assignments relating to limited company clients.

TASKS

1 The following trial balance has been extracted from the books of account for Sharjah plc as at 31 May 20-7:

	Dr	Cr
	£000	£000
Administrative expenses	210	
Distribution costs	190	
Wages and salaries	350	
Directors fees	200	
Travel expenses	100	
Rent, rates and insurance	150	
General expenses	120	
Called up share capital		500
Debtors	500	
Cash at bank and in hand	50	
Share premium account		100
Land and buildings:		
At cost	1,000	
Accumulated depreciation (at 1 June 20-6)		100
Plant and equipment:		
At cost	800	
Accumulated depreciation (at 1 June 20-6)		320
Purchases	900	
Sales		2,500
Creditors		400
Stock (as at 1 June 20-6)	110	
Profit and loss account (as at 1 June 20-6)		760
	4,680	4,680

Additional information

- Closing stock at 31 May 20-7 was valued at £130,000.

- Corporation Tax based on the company's profits for the year was estimated to be £80,000.

- The company's authorised and Issued Share Capital consists of 1,000,000 Ordinary Shares of 50p each.

- A final Ordinary Dividend of 10p per share has been proposed.

- The company adopts the following policy with regard to depreciation:

    Land and buildings 2 per cent per annum on cost.

    Plant and equipment 20 per cent per annum on cost.

REQUIRED

(a) Prepare the company's trading, profit and loss account for the year to 31 May 20-7. (This is required for internal purposes only).

(b) Explain briefly how the balance on the share premium account arose.

2 You have been assigned to assist in the preparation of the financial statements of McTaggart Ltd for the year ended 30 September 20-7. The company markets and distributes its board game called 'The Absolute' to a worldwide market from its premises in Cambridge. You have been provided with an extract from the extended trial balance of McTaggart Ltd on 30 September 20-7 (set out on the next page).

You have been given the following further information:

- The authorised share capital of the business, all of which has been issued, consists of ordinary shares with a nominal value of £1.

- Depreciation has been calculated on all of the fixed assets of the business and has already been entered on a monthly basis into the distribution costs and administration expenses ledger balances as shown on the extended trial balance.

- The corporation tax charge for the year has been calculated as £1,113,000.

- The company has paid an interim dividend of 8p per share during the year but has not provided for the proposed final dividend of 12p per share.

- Interest on the long term loan has now been paid for the last month of the year. The interest charge for September 20-7 amounts to £26,000.

REQUIRED

Taking into account the further information provided, draft a profit and loss account for the year ended 30 September 20-7 and a balance sheet as at that date, according to the Companies Act 1985 and FRS 3 (revised).

Notes

- You are not required to produce journal entries for any adjustments to the figures in the extended trial balance, but you may find them useful as working notes.

- Ignore any effect of these adjustments on the tax charge for the year as given above.

EXTENDED TRIAL BALANCE (extract)	name: McTaggart Ltd		date: 30 September 20-7	
Description	**Profit and loss**		**Balance sheet**	
	Dr *£000*	*Cr* *£000*	*Dr* *£000*	*Cr* *£000*
Trade creditors				1,891
Profit and loss account				2,159
Interim dividend	240			
Land – cost			1,820	
Buildings – cost			2,144	
Fixtures and fittings – cost			1,704	
Motor vehicles – cost			1,931	
Office equipment – cost			236	
Trade debtors			2,191	
Interest charges	166			
Sales		15,373		
Accruals				145
Provision for doubtful debts				85
Distribution costs	2,033			
Administrative expenses	1,562			
Stock	2,034	4,731	4,731	
Cash at bank and in hand			1,086	
Long term loan				2,750
Returns inwards	95			
Returns outwards		157		
Buildings – accumulated depreciation				872
Fixtures and fittings – accumulated dep'n				898
Motor vehicles – accumulated dep'n				1,027
Office equipment – accumulated dep'n				88
Ordinary share capital				3,000
Purchases	11,166			
Prepayments			37	
Profit	2,965			2,965
	20,261	20,261	15,880	15,880

3 You have been assigned to assist in the preparation of the financial statements of Primavera Fashions Ltd for the year ended 31 March 20-7. The company is a trading company which distributes fashion clothing.

Primavera Fashions Ltd recently engaged a financial accountant to manage a team of book-keepers. The book-keepers produced a correct extended trial balance of the company and gave it to the accountant so that he could draft the year-end financial statements.

The book-keeping staff have reported that he appeared to have some difficulty with the task and, after several days, apparently gave up the task and has not been seen since. He left behind him a balance sheet and some pages of workings which appear to contain a number of errors.

There is to be a meeting of the Board next week at which the financial statements will be approved. You have been brought in to assist in the production of a corrected balance sheet and to advise the directors on matters concerning the year end accounts. The uncorrected balance sheet, the workings left by the financial accountant and an extract from the extended trial balance (which *is* correct) of Primavera Fashions Ltd on 31 March 20-7 are set out on the next three pages.

EXTENDED TRIAL BALANCE (extract)   name: Primavera Fashions Ltd   date: 31 March 20-7

Description	Profit and loss		Balance sheet	
	Dr £000	Cr £000	Dr £000	Cr £000
Profit and loss account				2,819
Land – cost			525	
Buildings – cost			1,000	
Fixtures and fittings – cost			1,170	
Motor vehicles – cost			1,520	
Office equipment			350	
Sales		12,604		
Buildings – accumulated depreciation				220
Fixtures and fittings – accumulated dep'n				346
Motor vehicles – accumulated dep'n				583
Office equipment – accumulated dep'n				143
Stock	1,097	1,178	1,178	
Interest charges	153			
Goodwill			128	
Trade debtors			857	
Purchases	7,604			
Interim dividend	160			
Investments			2,924	
Cash at bank			152	
Distribution costs	1,495			
Administrative expenses	1,457			
Depreciation – buildings	50			
Depreciation – fixtures and fittings	117			
Depreciation – motor vehicles	380			
Depreciation – office equipment	70			
Share capital				1,000
Provision for doubtful debts				61
Trade creditors				483
Accruals				104
Dividends from subsidiary undertaking		23		
Prepayments			37	
Dividends from associated company		10		
10 per cent Debentures				1,500
Share premium				800
Revaluation reserve				550
Profit	1,232			1,232
	13,815	13,815	9,841	9,841

Primavera Fashions Ltd

Balance Sheet as at 31 March 20-7

	£000	£000
Fixed assets		
Intangible assets		128
Tangible assets		3,948
Investments		2,924
		7,000
Current assets		
Stocks	1,097	
Debtors	924	
Cash at bank and in hand	152	
	2,173	
Creditors: amounts falling due within one year	2,486	
Net current assets (liabilities)		(313)
Total assets less current liabilities		6,687
Creditors: amounts falling due after more than one year		800
		5,887
Capital and reserves		
Called up share capital		1,000
Revaluation reserve		550
Profit and loss account		4,051
		5,601

Workings

1. Fixed Assets:

	Cost	Acc. Depn.	NBV
	£000	£000	£000
Land	525	-	525
Buildings	1,000	50	950
Fixtures and fittings	1,170	117	1,053
Motor vehicles	1,520	380	1,140
Office equipment	350	70	280
	4,565	617	3,948

2. Debtors:

	£000	£000
Trade debtors	857	
plus Accruals	104	
		961
less Prepayments		(37)
		924

3. Creditors (amounts falling due within one year):

	£000
Trade creditors	483
Corporation tax payable	382
Dividends payable	60
Provision for doubtful debts	61
10 per cent Debentures	1,500
	2,486

4. Creditors (amounts falling due after more than one year):

	£000
Share premium	800

5. Profit and Loss account:

	£000
At 1 April 20-6	2,819
Retained profit for the year	1,232
At 31 March 20-7	4,051

You have also received the following additional information to assist you in your task:

- The share capital consists of ordinary shares with a nominal value of 25 pence. The company has paid an interim dividend during the year and the directors have recommended a final dividend of 6 pence per share, which has not been provided for in the extended trial balance.

- The tax charge for the year has been estimated at £382,000.

- The investments shown on the extended trial balance relate to long term investment in the shares of one subsidiary undertaking and one associated company.

REQUIRED

Redraft the company balance sheet for Primavera Fashions Ltd as at 31 March 20-7. Make any changes that you feel to be necessary to the balance sheet and workings provided by the disappearing financial accountant using the information contained in the extended trial balance for the year ended 31 March 20-7 and the additional information provided above. The balance sheet should meet the requirements of the Companies Act 1985 and FRS 3 (revised).

ADVISING ON ACCOUNTING POLICIES

4

SITUATION

You work for the accounting firm Wasserman Pricehaus. You have a number of clients who find it difficult understanding accounting concepts and the idea of accounting for assets and liabilities and profit. Last week you had three clients with queries about their financial statements.

TASKS

1   Joseph Coxhead is the owner of his own fine art gallery business. He has recently received his latest set of financial statements and has prepared a list of questions and queries for your attention.

The questions are as follows:

(a)   Why doesn't my balance sheet show my personal home as a fixed asset? I conduct a lot of my business meetings and entertaining there, as well as producing a number of sketches in my spare time.

(b)   I have wanted to value all my art paintings this year at selling price, rather than cost price as this will give a higher net profit figure – and impress my bank manager!

(c)   Last year I used the reducing balance method to calculate the depreciation on my works van, however this year I wanted to change to the straight line method as this will reduce the charge for depreciation and again increase my overall profit figure.

(d)   I was keen during the year to keep my drawings to a minimum, again to achieve as high as profit figure as possible. Hopefully this strategy has now paid off in the accounts.

(e)   I suspect that when I built the extension to the art gallery this year, some of the invoices were entered into the 'Art Gallery at cost' account, but some of the others were entered into the 'Buildings repairs and maintenance' account. However I don't think that this matters too much as it will all be written off to the profit and loss account eventually anyway.

REQUIRED

Comment on each of the points listed above made by Joseph and in each case where relevant refer to the relevant accounting concepts, SSAP's and FRS's.

2   You have received the following comments and suggestions from the Finance Director of Mason Holdings plc at a meeting held to discuss the information needed for the year's draft accounts:

(a)   "There is no point in depreciating the freehold buildings because the market value must be considerably in excess of its cost."

(b)   "I see that our investment property held in Guildford has not been depreciated this year at all. I suggest we depreciate it at the same rate as all our other properties in line with the consistency concept in accountancy."

(c)   "We have just received a government grant for the new warehouse we have purchased in Merthyr Tydfill. I suggest we reduce the acquisition cost accordingly and depreciate the asset on the reduced amount, rather than using the deferred credit method, which looks too complicated to deal with!"

(d)   "The applied research undertaken by the company this year should be carried forward on the balance sheet this year as a deferred development cost. I know that the product is only at its early stages but I am hopeful that the project is a good idea and it could work for us in the future."

(e)   "During the year we acquired another company leading to some purchased goodwill. I suggest we write this off immediately to our reserves. There is no point in carrying forward in the accounts an asset that does not exist."

(f)   "This year we leased all of our vehicles under a finance lease for the first time. Reading through the contract, I see that the vehicles do not legally become ours until the final installment has been paid, and then only when the option to purchase payment has been made. I therefore suggest that we treat all the payments made as a form of rent and charge them to the profit and loss account accordingly."

REQUIRED

How would you reply to each of these points raised by the Finance Director? In each case offer advice as to the best accounting practice to be followed. You will need to refer to the relevant SSAP's and FRS's where applicable.

3   The directors of Maximilian PLC are about to approve the financial statements for the current year ending 31 August. Since the accounts were prepared, the following additional information has now been made available. Assume the date today is 19 October.

(a)   On 16 October an electrical fire caused severe damage to the company's factory which is likely to make the manufacturing process inoperable for the next three months.

(b)   The year-end debtor balances include a debt of £15,000 from a customer who has been made bankrupt on 14 October. It is unlikely that any money will be received from this account.

(c)   The company is currently awaiting the outcome of a legal suit. An independent lawyer has assessed that it is probable that Maximilian PLC will receive £100,000 from it.

(d)   The company is expecting to receive an order from Tokyo in the next few days worth £10 million based on a new product which the company has just marketed and released.

(e)   A former employee is currently involved with legal action against the company over an alleged assault which took place after the Christmas party. The case is proving difficult to prove and the company's solicitors recommend that there is no likelihood of this action succeeding.

REQUIRED

Advise the directors, giving your reasons, as to how these situations should be dealt with in the company's financial statements for the year ended 31 August. Wherever possible you should refer to the relevant SSAP's and FRS's.

CASH FLOW STATEMENTS AND RATIOS

5

SITUATION

You are a trainee in the accounting firm Henman Osborne & Co. Your supervisor has handed you a couple of assignments which include a cash flow statement and a ratios calculation. You are to carry out the tasks set and will then hand them to your supervisor so that he can see how you are getting on.

TASKS

1   You have been given the financial statements of Edlin Ltd for the year ended 31 March 20-6, with comparative figures for the year ended 31 March 20-5. The company is expanding and is in the middle of a major programme of replacing all of its fixed assets.

Edlin Ltd

Profit and loss account for the year ended 31 March 20-6

	20-6		20-5	
	£000	£000	£000	£000
Turnover, continuing operations		3,000		2,000
Opening stock	200		150	
Purchases	1,700		1,250	
Closing stock	(220)		(200)	
		1,680		1,200
Gross profit		1,320		800
Depreciation		175		150
Other expenses		500		400
Profit on sale of fixed asset		5		
Operating profit for the year		650		250
Interest paid		15		12
Profit before tax		635		238
Taxation on profit		100		35
Profit after tax		535		203
Proposed dividends		100		50
Retained profit		435		153
Retained profit (loss) b/f		115		(38)
Retained profit c/f		550		115

Edlin Ltd

Balance sheet as at 31 March 20-6

	20-6 £000	20-6 £000	20-5 £000	20-5 £000
Fixed assets		552		200
Current assets				
Stock	220		200	
Debtors	250		160	
Cash	218		20	
	688		380	
Current liabilities				
Trade creditors	150		110	
Dividends payable	100		50	
Taxation	100		35	
	350		195	
Net current assets		338		185
Total assets less current liabilities		890		385
Long-term liabilities				
Long-term loan		150		120
		740		265
Financed by:				
Capital reserves				
Called up share capital	120		100	
Share premium account	70		50	
Profit and loss account	550		115	
		740		265

The following further information is provided:

* In July 20-5 an asset was sold which had originally cost £20,000 when it was purchased by the company in July 20-2. Fixed assets are depreciated on a straightline basis at 20%. The policy is to charge a full year's depreciation in the year of purchase and none in the year of sale.

* A new asset was purchased for £535,000 during the year.

* Sales and purchases were on credit with all other expenses (including interest) being paid in cash.

* There was a share issue during the year.

REQUIRED

(a) Prepare a reconciliation between cash flows from operating activities and operating profit for the year ended 31 March 20-6.

(b) Prepare a cash flow statement for the year ended 31 March 20-6 in accordance with FRS 1 (Revised).

2   Botticelli Ltd is a trading company that sells carpets to retail outlets. The shareholders of Botticelli Ltd have some questions about the profitability and liquidity of the company. The profit and loss account and balance sheet produced for internal purposes are set out below.

Botticelli Ltd
Profit and loss account for the year ended 31 December 20-6

	20-6		20-5	
	£000	£000	£000	£000
Turnover		2,963		1,736
Opening stock	341		201	
Purchases	1,712		1,097	
Closing stock	(419)		(341)	
Cost of sales		1,634		957
Gross profit		1,329		779
Depreciation		247		103
Other expenses		588		334
Profit on the sale of fixed assets		15		
Operating profit for the year		509		342
Interest paid		78		26
Profit before tax		431		316
Taxation on profit		138		111
Profit after tax		293		205
Ordinary dividend		48		22
Retained profit		245		183

Botticelli Ltd
Balance sheet as at 31 December 20-6

	20-6	20-5
	£000	£000
Fixed assets	2,800	1,013
Current assets		
Stocks	419	341
Debtors	444	381
Cash		202
	863	924
Current liabilities		
Trade creditors	322	197
Dividends payable	48	41
Taxation	158	103
Bank overdraft	194	
	722	341

Net current assets	141	583
Total assets less current liabilities	2,941	1,596
Long-term loan	970	320
	1,971	1,276
Capital and reserves		
Called up share capital	400	200
Share premium	250	
Profit and loss account	1,321	1,076
	1,971	1,276

REQUIRED

Prepare a preliminary draft report to the shareholders about the profitability and liquidity of Botticelli Ltd for the two years, 20-5 and 20-6. Your report should include:

(a)   calculation of the following ratios for the two years:

- return on capital employed

- gross profit ratio

- net profit ratio

- current ratio

- quick ratio (also called acid test)

(b)   comments on the changes in the ratios from 20-5 to 20-6.

CONSOLIDATED ACCOUNTS

6

SITUATION

You work for the accounting firm Clarke Paul & Co. You have been handed a number of assignments relating to groups of companies. The tasks involve preparing consolidated accounts and advising on policy.

TASKS

1   You have been sent the following summarised balance sheets for the Rain group of companies as at 30 September 20-4

	Rain PLC	Sleet PLC
	£000	£000
FIXED ASSETS		
Plant and equipment at net book value	236	30
Investment :		
40,000 ordinary shares of £1 each in Sleet PLC	184	
	420	30
CURRENT ASSETS		
Stock	150	80
Debtors	250	20
Cash at bank and in hand	50	10
	450	110
CURRENT LIABILITIES		
Creditors	(280)	(20)
	590	120
CAPITAL AND RESERVES		
Issued and fully paid ordinary shares of £1 each	500	50
Profit and loss account	90	70
	590	120

Additional information

- Rain acquired its shares in Sleet on 1 October 20-1 when Sleet's profit and loss account amounted to £30,000.

- The respective company's debtors and creditors at 30 September 20-4 include the following inter-company debt:

  Sleet owed Rain £5,000

- Any goodwill arising on consolidation is to be amortised on a straight-line basis over a ten year period.

REQUIRED

Prepare Rain's consolidated balance sheet as at 30 September 20-4. The balance sheet is not required for publication purposes.

2   You are presented with the following summarised profit and loss accounts for Norberry PLC and its subsidiary Manberry Ltd.

Profit and loss accounts for the year ending 30 September 20-4.

	Norberry PLC	Manberry Ltd
	£000	£000
Turnover, continuing operations	1,700	450
Cost of sales	920	75
	780	375
Distribution costs	100	75
Administrative expenses	200	100
OPERATING PROFIT	480	200
Income from shares in group company	120	
Profit on ordinary activities before taxation	600	200
Tax on ordinary profits	30	20
Profit on ordinary activities after taxation	570	180
Dividends	360	150
Retained profit for the year	210	30

Additional information

- Norberry PLC acquired 80% of the shares in Manberry Ltd on 1 October 20-1.

- During the year Norberry PLC sold stock which had cost £100,000 to Manberry Ltd for £110,000. All of the stock had been sold by Manberry Ltd by the end of the year.

- Any goodwill arising on consolidation is considered to have an indefinite life, so any write off for goodwill can be ignored for the above period.

REQUIRED

(a)   Draft a consolidated profit and loss account for Norberry PLC and its subsidiary undertaking for the year ended 30 September 20-4

(b)   One of the directors subsequently telephoned asking about the entries for goodwill and minority interest. Briefly explain what both of these terms mean in relation to the consolidated balance sheet.

3   You are handed a query about the accounting treatment of associated companies. Charlton Ltd purchased 30 per cent of the ordinary share capital of Kingley Ltd for £280,000 on 1 April 20-8. Kingley Ltd is an associated undertaking and the directors would like to know how Kingley Ltd would be included in the consolidated profit and loss account and consolidated balance sheet of the Charlton Group. Extracts from Kingley Ltd's financial statements are given below:

Profit and loss account of Kingley Ltd for the year ended 31 March 20-9

	£000
Net profit before tax	350
Taxation	95
Net profit after tax	255

Balance sheet of Kingley Ltd as at 31 March 20-9

	£000
Fixed assets	800
Net current assets	150
	950
Long term liability	70
	880
Financed by:	
Ordinary share capital	300
Share premium	70
Profit and loss account	510
	880

Notes
* no shares were issued in the year ended 31 March 20-9
* no dividends were paid or proposed in that year
* all assets of Kingley Ltd are stated at fair values
* goodwill is deemed to have an indefinite useful economic life and should not, therefore, be amortised

REQUIRED

What figures would be shown in the consolidated profit and loss account and consolidated balance sheet of the Charlton Group for the year ended 31 March 20-9 to account for the results of the associate Kingley Ltd?

4   The Managing Director of Predator Limited, one of your clients, telephones to say that his company is about to acquire a majority shareholding in Minimus Limited. He has heard that the idea of 'Fair Value' is very important when it comes to asset valuation in a takeover situation.

Explain the concept of fair value in relation to an acquisition of another company.

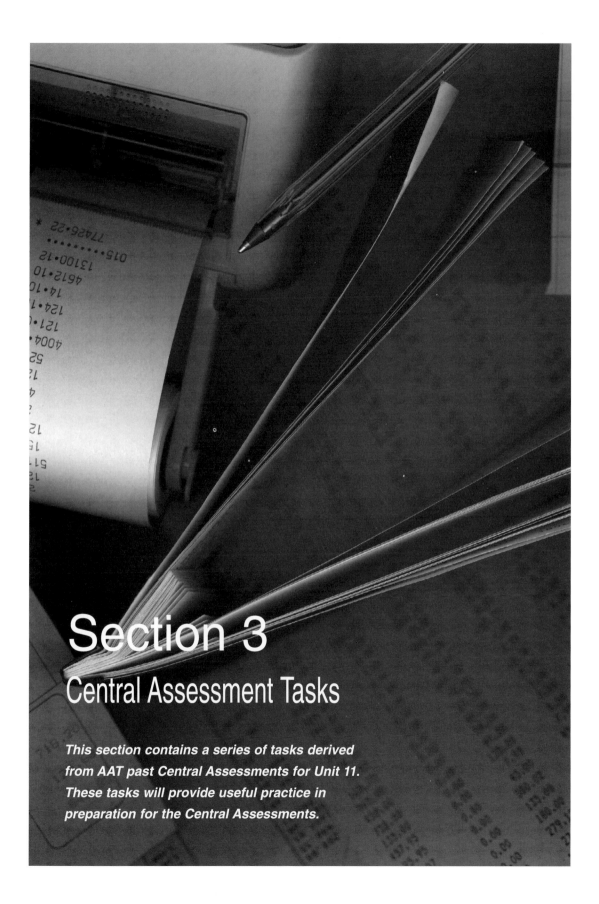

Section 3
Central Assessment Tasks

*This section contains a series of tasks derived
from AAT past Central Assessments for Unit 11.
These tasks will provide useful practice in
preparation for the Central Assessments.*

CENTRAL ASSESSMENT TASKS

contents

a note on practising Central Assessment Tasks

The practice tasks in the Central Assessments in this Section have been adapted from AAT past Central Assessments. Osborne Books would like to thank AAT for giving permission for the use of their material in this way. In a number of cases names, dates and numbers have been changed to provide consistency of presentation.

As far as possible the guidance timings have been preserved and the 'proforma' documents found in the AAT answer booklets have been reproduced to enable students to gain familiarity with the way a Central Assessment 'works'.

An important note of caution: AAT are rightly anxious to point out that students should not 'question spot' likely topics for assessment and ignore other topics. They do so at their peril. Students should cover all areas of the specifications and so be technically competent in their studies – and in their work.

Central Assessment Tasks

Practice Central Assessment 1

recommended timing 3 hours plus 15 minutes reading time

SECTION 1

You are advised to spend approximately 55 minutes on this section.

Data

Magnus Carter has recently inherited a majority shareholding in a company, Baron Ltd. The company supplies camping equipment to retail outlets. Magnus wishes to get involved in the management of the business, but until now he has only worked in not-for-profit organisations. He would like to understand how the company has performed over the past two years and how efficient it is in using its resources. He has asked you to help him to interpret the financial statements of the company which are set out below.

Baron Ltd

Summary Profit and Loss Account

for the year ended 31 March

	20-1	20-0
	£000	£000
Turnover	1,852	1,691
Cost of sales	648	575
Gross profit	1,204	1,116
Expenses	685	524
Profit before tax	519	592
Tax	125	147
Profit after tax	394	445
Dividends	250	325
Retained profit	144	120

Baron Ltd

Summary Balance Sheets as at 31 March

	20-1		20-0	
	£000	£000	£000	£000
Fixed assets		1,431		1,393
Current assets				
Stocks	217		159	
Debtors	319		236	
Cash	36		147	
	572		542	

Current liabilities

Trade Creditors	48		44
Proposed dividend	250		325
Taxation	125		130
	423		499
Net current assets		149	43
		1,580	1,436
Share capital		500	500
Profit and loss account		1,080	936
		1,580	1,436

Task 1.1

Prepare a report for Magnus Carter that includes:

(a)　a calculation of the following ratios for the two years:

　　(i)　Gross profit percentage

　　(ii)　Net profit percentage

　　(iii)　Debtor turnover in days (debtor payment period)

　　(iv)　Creditor turnover in days (creditor payment period based on cost of sales)

　　(v)　Stock turnover in days (stock turnover period based on cost of sales)

(b)　for each ratio calculated:

　　(i)　a brief explanation in general terms of the meaning of the ratio

　　(ii)　comments on how the performance or efficiency in the use of resources has changed over the two years

(c)　a statement, with reasons, identifying the areas that could be improved over the next year as indicated by the ratios and analysis performed

Task 1.2

Prepare brief notes to answer the following questions asked by Magnus:

(a)　"How can the accounting equation in a company balance when, unlike a not-for-profit organisation, there are no funds to balance net assets on its balance sheet?"

(b)　"Can you give me two examples of users outside of the company, other than myself and the other shareholders, who may be interested in the financial statements of Baron Ltd. For each user can you tell me for what purpose they would use them?"

SECTION 2

You are advised to spend approximately 125 minutes on this section.

This section is in three parts.

PART A

Data

The directors of Machier Ltd have asked you to assist them in producing a cash flow statement for the year ended 31 March 20-9 using the information in the balance sheet and profit and loss account shown on the next two pages.

The following further information is also provided:

*   fixed assets costing £28,000 with accumulated depreciation of £19,000 were sold in the year

*   all sales and purchases were on credit; other expenses were paid for in cash

The directors have also been in negotiation with the directors of another company, Papier Ltd, about the possibility of Papier Ltd buying 75 per cent of the share capital of Machier Ltd. If the acquisition goes ahead, Papier Ltd will pay £1,761,000 for the shares based on the value of the company as at 31 March 20-9. The fair value of the fixed assets in Machier Ltd at 31 March 20-9, the agreed date of acquisition, is £4,682,000. All of the other assets and liabilities are stated at fair value. There is a meeting of the directors of both companies shortly. The directors of Machier Ltd wish you to attend this meeting to explain some of the accounting issues involved in the acquisition of Machier Ltd by Papier Ltd.

Task 2.1

Provide a reconciliation between cash flows from operating activities and operating profit of Machier Ltd for the year ended 31 March 20-9.

Task 2.2

Using the pro-forma provided on page 117 prepare a cash flow statement for Machier Ltd for the year ended 31 March 20-9 in accordance with the requirements of FRS1 (Revised).

Task 2.3

Calculate the goodwill on consolidation that would arise on acquisition if Papier Ltd had purchased 75 per cent of the shares in Machier Ltd on 31 March 20-9.

Note: you are not required to produce a consolidated balance sheet for the group.

Task 2.4

In a note to the directors, explain the options that are available for the accounting treatment of goodwill arising on acquisition in group accounts.

Machier Ltd

Profit and Loss account for the year ended 31 March 20-9

	20-9	20-8
	£000	£000
Turnover	2,636	1,687
Cost of sales	923	590
Gross profit	1,713	1,097
Depreciation	856	475
Other expenses	126	101
Profit on the sale of fixed assets	7	2
Operating profit for the year	738	523
Interest paid	252	120
Profit before tax	486	403
Taxation on profit	165	137
Profit after tax	321	266
Ordinary dividend	40	20
Retained profit	281	246
Retained profit brought forward	1,127	881
Retained profit carried forward	1,408	1,127

Machier Ltd
Balance sheet as at 31 March 20-9

	20-9	20-8
	£000	£000
Fixed assets	4,282	2,376
Current assets		
Stocks	448	287
Debtors	527	337
Cash	–	86
	975	710
Current liabilities		
Trade creditors	381	212
Dividends payable	20	10
Taxation	165	137
Bank overdraft	183	–
	749	359
Net current assets	226	351
Long term loan	2,800	1,500
	1,708	1,227
Capital and reserves		
Called up share capital	200	100
Share premium	100	–
Profit and loss account	1,408	1,127
	1,708	1,227

Pro-forma Cash Flow Statement

(in accordance with FRS1 (Revised))

£000

Net Cash inflow from operating activities

Returns on investments and servicing of finance

Taxation

Capital expenditure

_____

Equity dividends paid

_____

Management of liquid resources

Financing

Increase /(decrease) in cash

_____

PART B

Data

You have been assigned to assist in the preparation of the financial statements of Typeset Ltd for the year ended 31 March 20-9. The company is a wholesale distributor of desktop publishing equipment. You have been provided with the extended trial balance of Typeset Ltd as at 31 March 20-9.

EXTENDED TRIAL BALANCE — name: Typeset Limited — date: 31 March 20-9

Description	Trial balance Dr £000	Trial balance Cr £000	Adjustments Dr £000	Adjustments Cr £000	Profit and loss Dr £000	Profit and loss Cr £000	Balance sheet Dr £000	Balance sheet Cr £000
Trade debtors	3,136						3,136	
Cash at bank	216						216	
Interest	125				125			
Profit and loss account		3,533						3,533
Provision for doubtful debts		37						37
Distribution costs	3,549		59	36	3,572			
Administration expenses	3,061		63	61	3,063			
Revaluation reserve		500						500
Sales		18,757				18,757		
Land - cost	2,075						2,075	
Buildings - cost	2,077						2,077	
Fixtures and fittings - cost	1,058						1,058	
Motor vehicles - cost	2,344						2,344	
Office equipment - cost	533						533	
Stock	3,921		4,187	4,187	3,921	4,187	4,187	
Purchases	10,582				10,582			
Interim dividend	250				250			
Trade creditors		1,763						1,763
Buildings - accumulated depreciation		383						383
Fixtures and fittings - accumulated dep'n		495						495
Motor vehicles - accumulated dep'n		1,237						1,237
Office equipment - accumulated dep'n		152						152
Prepayments			97				97	
Ordinary share capital		5,000						5,000
Share premium		1,200						1,200
Accruals				122				122
Investments	1,580						1,580	
Long term loan		1,450						1,450
Profit					1,431			1,431
Total	34,507	34,507	4,406	4,406	22,944	22,944	17,303	17,303

You have been given the following further information:

* The authorised share capital of the business, all of which has been issued, consists of ordinary shares with a nominal value of £1.

* Depreciation has been calculated on a monthly basis on all of the fixed assets of the business and has already been entered into the distribution costs and administration expenses ledger balances as shown on the extended trial balance.

* The corporation tax charge for the year has been calculated as £493,000.

* The company has paid an interim dividend of 5p per share during the year but has not provided for the proposed final dividend of 7p per share.

* One of the customers who owed the company £36,000 at the end of the year is in financial difficulties. The directors have estimated that only half of this amount is likely to be paid. No adjustment has been made for this in the extended trial balance. The general provision for doubtful debts is to be maintained at 2 per cent of the remaining debtors excluding the £36,000 balance.

Task 2.5

Using the pro-forma provided on the next page, make any adjustments required as a result of the further information provided and draft a balance sheet for Typeset Ltd as at 31 March 20-9.

Notes:

* You are not required to produce notes to the accounts.

* You are not required to produce journal entries for any adjustments to the figures in the extended trial balance that are required.

* You should ignore any effect of these adjustments on the tax charge for the year as given above.

Pro-forma Balance Sheet (Format 1)

Fixed Assets

    Intangible assets

    Tangible assets

    Investments   _____

Current Assets

    Stock

    Debtors

    Investments

    Cash at bank and in hand   _____

Creditors: amounts falling due within one year   _____

Net current assets (liabilities)   _____

Total assets *less* current liabilities

Creditors: amounts falling due after more than one year

Provision for liabilities and charges   _____

    _____

Capital and reserves

    _____

PART C

Data

Mary Rose, Nelson Victory and Elizabeth Second are in partnership together hiring out river boats. Mary has decided to retire from the partnership at the end of the day on 31 March 20-9. You have been asked to finalise the partnership accounts for the year ended 31 March 20-9 and to make the entries necessary to account for the retirement of Mary from the partnership on that day.

You have been given the following information:

1) The profit for the year ended 31 March 20-9 was £106,120.

2) The partners are entitled to the following salaries per annum:

Mary	£18,000
Nelson	£16,000
Elizabeth	£13,000

3) Interest on capital is to be paid at a rate of 12 per cent on the balance at the beginning of the year on the capital accounts. No interest is paid on the current accounts.

4) Cash drawings in the year amounted to:

Mary	£38,000
Nelson	£30,000
Elizabeth	£29,000

5) The balances on the current and capital accounts at 1 April 20-8 were as follows:

Capital accounts:		Current accounts:	
Mary	£28,000 Cr	Mary	£2,500 Cr
Nelson	£26,000 Cr	Nelson	£2,160 Cr
Elizabeth	£22,000 Cr	Elizabeth	£1,870 Cr

6) The profit sharing ratios in the partnership are currently:

Mary	4/10
Nelson	3/10
Elizabeth	3/10

On the retirement of Mary, Nelson will put a further £40,000 of capital into the business. The new profit sharing ratios will be:

Nelson	6/10
Elizabeth	4/10

7) The goodwill in the partnership is to be valued at £90,000 on 31 March 20-9. No separate account for goodwill is to be maintained in the books of the partnership. Any adjusting entries in respect of goodwill are to be made in the capital accounts of the partners.

8) The partners have had the assets of the partnership valued at 31 March 20-9. The book value of the assets at that date and the valuation are as follows:

	Book Value	Valuation
	£	£
Land and buildings	278,000	328,000
Debtors	36,000	26,000

The valuations are to remain in the books of the new partnership.

9) Any amounts to the credit of Mary on the date of her retirement should be transferred to a loan account.

Task 2.6

Prepare the partners' capital accounts as at 31 March 20-9 showing the adjustments that need to be made on the retirement of Mary from the partnership.

Task 2.7

Prepare an appropriation account for the partnership for the year ended 31 March 20-9.

Task 2.8

Prepare the partners' current accounts for the year ended 31 March 20-9.

Task 2.9

Show the balance on Mary's loan account as at 31 March 20-9.

Task 2.10

Draft a letter to the partners explaining briefly, and giving reasons for, the adjustments that you have made to the capital accounts of the partners on the retirement of Mary from the partnership on 31 March 20-9.

Central Assessment Tasks

Practice Central Assessment 2

recommended timing 3 hours plus 15 minutes reading time

SECTION 1

You are advised to spend approximately 55 minutes on this section.

Data

Page Ltd is a company that supplies stationery for business and domestic purposes. You have been asked to assist the directors in the interpretation of the financial statements of the company. They are intending to apply to the bank for a substantial loan. The bank has asked them for their financial statements for the last two years. The directors wish to know how the bank will view their profitability, liquidity and financial position on the evidence of these financial statements.

The directors are also concerned that they do not fully understand the financial statements of customers to whom they supply stationery. The customers include public sector and other not-for-profit organisations.

You have been supplied with the profit and loss account and the balance sheet of Page Ltd for two years, prepared for internal purposes.

Page Ltd

Profit and Loss account for the year ended 31 March 20-9

	20-9	20-8
	£000	£000
Turnover	2,636	1,687
Cost of sales	923	590
Gross profit	1,713	1,097
Depreciation	856	475
Other expenses	126	101
Profit on the sale of fixed assets	7	2
Operating profit for the year	738	523
Interest paid	252	120
Profit before tax	486	403
Taxation on profit	165	137
Profit after tax	321	266
Ordinary dividend	40	20
Retained profit	281	246
Retained profit brought forward	1,127	881
Retained profit carried forward	1,408	1,127

Page Ltd
Balance sheet as at 31 March 20-9

	20-9	20-8
	£000	£000
Fixed assets	4,282	2,376
Current assets		
Stocks	448	287
Debtors	527	337
Cash	–	86
	975	710
Current liabilities		
Trade creditors	381	212
Dividends payable	20	10
Taxation	165	137
Bank overdraft	183	–
	749	359
Net current assets	226	351
Long term loan	2,800	1,500
	1,708	1,227
Capital and reserves		
Called up share capital	200	100
Share premium	100	–
Profit and loss account	1,408	1,127
	1,708	1,227

Task 1.1

Prepare a report for the directors which includes the following:

(a)   a calculation of the following ratios of Page Ltd for the two years:

(i)   Return on equity
(ii)   Net profit percentage
(iii)   Quick ratio/acid test
(iv)   Gearing ratio
(v)   Interest cover

(b)   comments on the profitability, liquidity and the financial position of the company as revealed by the ratios and a statement of how this has changed over the two years covered by the financial statements

(c)   an opinion as to whether the bank would be likely to give the company a substantial loan based solely on the information in the financial statements

Task 1.2

The Accounting Standards Board's Statement of Principles for Financial Reporting states that:

> *"The objective of financial statements is to provide information about the reporting entity's financial performance and financial position that is useful to a wide range of users for assessing the stewardship of management and for making economic decisions."*

Illustrate this objective by:

either

(a)   selecting one external user of financial statements from profit making organisations or public sector/not-for-profit organisations and showing how it uses financial statements to assess the stewardship of management

or

(b)   selecting one external user of financial statements from profit-making organisations or public sector/not-for-profit organisations and showing how it uses financial statements to make economic decisions

SECTION 2

You are advised to spend approximately 125 minutes on this section.

This section is in three parts.

PART A

You are advised to spend approximately 40 minutes on this part.

Data

You have been asked to assist in the preparation of the consolidated accounts of the Bloomsbury Group. Set out on the next page are the balance sheets of Woolf Ltd and Forster Ltd for the year ended 31 March 20-1:

Balance Sheets as at 31 March 20-1

	Woolf Ltd		Forster Ltd	
	£000	£000	£000	£000
Tangible fixed assets		12,995		1,755
Investment in Forster Ltd		1,978		–
Current assets				
Stocks	3,586		512	
Debtors	2,193		382	
Cash	84		104	
	5,863		998	
Current liabilities				
Trade Creditors	1,920		273	
Proposed dividend	160		–	
Taxation	667		196	
	2,747		469	
Net current assets		3,116		529
Long term loan		–		(400)
		18,089		1,884
Share capital		2,000		1,000
Share premium		–		200
Profit and loss account		16,089		684
		18,089		1,884

Further information:

- The share capital of both Woolf Ltd and Forster Ltd consists of ordinary shares of £1 each. There have been no changes to the balances of share capital and share premium during the year. No dividends were paid by Forster Ltd during the year.

- Woolf Ltd acquired 750,000 shares in Forster Ltd on 31 March 20-0.

- At 31 March 20-0 the balance on the profit and loss account of Forster Ltd was £424,000.

- The fair value of the fixed assets of Forster Ltd at 31 March 20-0 was £2,047,000 as compared with their book value of £1,647,000. The revaluation has not been reflected in the books of Forster Ltd. (Ignore any depreciation implications).

- Goodwill arising on consolidation is to be amortised using the straight-line method over a period of 10 years.

Task 2.1

Using the pro-forma provided on the next page prepare the consolidated balance sheet of Woolf Ltd and its subsidiary undertaking as at 31 March 20-1.

Pro-forma Balance Sheet (Format 1)

Fixed Assets

    Intangible assets

    Tangible assets

    Investments   _____

Current Assets

    Stock

    Debtors

    Investments

    Cash at bank and in hand   _____

Creditors: amounts falling due within one year   _____

Net current assets (liabilities)   _____

Total assets *less* current liabilities

Creditors: amounts falling due after more than one year

Provision for liabilities and charges   _____

    _____

Capital and reserves

    _____

Minority interest

    _____

    _____

PART B

You are advised to spend approximately 45 minutes on this part.

Data

You have been asked to assist in the preparation of financial statements for Angle Ltd for the year ended 31 March 20-1. The profit and loss account and balance sheets of the company are set out below.

Angle Ltd

Profit and Loss Account for the year ended 31 March 20-1

	20-1
	£000
Turnover, continuing operations	8,975
Cost of sales	5,013
Gross profit	3,962
Distribution costs	1,172
Administration expenses	953
Operating profit, continuing operations	1,837
Interest paid and similar charges	202
Profit on ordinary activities before taxation	1,635
Tax on profit on ordinary activities	490
Profit for the financial year	1,145
Dividends	450
Retained profit for the financial year	695

Angle Ltd

Balance Sheet as at 31 March 20-1

	20-1	20-1	20-0	20-0
	£000	£000	£000	£000
Fixed assets		7,287		4,009
Current assets				
Stocks	1,982		1,346	
Trade debtors	812		1,086	
Cash	433		82	
	3,227		2,514	
Current liabilities				
Trade Creditors	423		397	
Dividends payable	450		400	
Taxation	490		370	
	1,363		1,167	

Net current assets	1,864	1,347
Long term loan	(2,500)	(1,500)
	6,651	3,856
Capital and reserves		
Called up share capital	3,000	2,200
Share premium	1,200	400
Revaluation reserve	500	–
Profit and loss account	1,951	1,256
	6,651	3,856

Further information

• Land included in the fixed assets was valued at market value at the end of the year by a professional valuer. The valuation has been incorporated into the financial statements of the company as at 31 March 20-1.

• No fixed assets were sold during the year to 31 March 20-1. Depreciation has been calculated on the fixed assets of the business and has already been entered in the profit and loss account. The charge for the year was £875,000.

• All sales and purchases were on credit. Other expenses were paid for in cash.

• Net cash inflow from operating activities for the year was £2,376,000.

• There was no over/underprovision of corporation tax for 20-0.

Task 2.2

Using the pro-forma provided on the next page, prepare a cash flow statement for Angle Ltd for the year ended 31 March 20-1 in accordance with the requirements of FRS 1 (Revised).

Notes:

• You are not required to provide a reconciliation between cash flows from operating activities and operating profit.

• You are not required to produce any of the notes required by FRS 1.

Task 2.3

Prepare a statement of total recognised gains and losses for the year ended 31 March 20-1 for Angle Ltd as required by FRS 3.

Data

FRS 3 requires separate disclosure of the results of continuing operations, acquisitions (as a component of continuing operations) and discontinued operations.

Task 2.4

Prepare notes to explain:

(a) what is meant, in FRS 3 by 'acquisitions' and 'discontinued operations'

(b) why it is useful to distinguish between the three types of operations for the purposes of financial reporting

Pro-forma Cash Flow Statement

(in accordance with FRS 1 (Revised))

£000

Net Cash inflow from operating activities

Returns on investments and servicing of finance

Taxation

Capital expenditure

_____

Equity dividends paid

_____

Management of liquid resources

Financing

Increase /(decrease) in cash

_____

PART C

You are advised to spend approximately 40 minutes on this part.

Data

Bess, Charles and George are in partnership together. They operate a retail jewellery business. They are considering dissolving the partnership next year. They have asked you to assist in the preparation of the year end financial statements of their business. The trial balance as at 31 March 20-1 is set out on the next page.

Bess, Charles and George

Trial Balance as at 31 March 20-1

	Debit	Credit
	£	£
Motor expenses	3,769	
Drawings – Bess	46,000	
Drawings – Charles	42,000	
Drawings – George	38,000	
Capital account – Bess		60,000
Capital account – Charles		40,000
Capital account – George		20,000
Sales		568,092
Returns outwards		7,004
Carriage inwards	872	
Trade creditors		9,904
Return inwards	8,271	
Purchases	302,117	
Carriage outwards	617	
Salespersons' commission	6,659	
Rent, rates and insurance	32,522	
Current account – Bess		4,670
Current account – Charles		5,600
Current account – George		3,750
Stock as at 1 April 20-0	127,535	
Motor vehicles at cost	37,412	
Office equipment at cost	2,363	
Fixtures and fittings at cost	8,575	
Staff wages and National Insurance Contribution	48,317	
Lighting and heating	3,240	
Postage and stationery	705	
Accumulated depreciation – motor vehicles		18,651
Accumulated depreciation – office equipment		1,285
Accumulated depreciation – fixtures and fittings		3,754
Depreciation charge – motor vehicles	4,765	
Depreciation charge – office equipment	236	
Depreciation charge – fixtures and fittings	1,613	
Telephone	2,926	
Sundries	868	
Cash at bank	23,980	
Cash in hand	228	
Accruals		880
	743,590	743,590

Further information:

- The stock at close of business on 31 March 20-1 was valued at cost at £143,936.

- The partners are entitled to the following salaries per annum:

    Bess   £30,000

    Charles   £25,000

    George   £17,000

- Interest on capital is to be paid to the partners at a rate of 5% on the balance at the end of the year on the capital accounts. No interest is to be paid on the current accounts.

- The profit sharing ratios in the partnership are:

    Bess   5/12

    Charles   4/12

    George   3/12

Task 2.5

Using the pro-forma on the next page, draft a profit and loss account for the year ended 31 March 20-1.

Task 2.6

Prepare an appropriation account for the partnership for the year ended 31 March 20-1.

Task 2.7

Draft notes to explain the accounting procedures that must be undertaken in order to dissolve the partnership.

Pro-forma Profit and loss account

(suitable for a partnership)

	£	£
Sales		
less Cost of Sales		
Gross profit		
less Expenses		
Net profit		

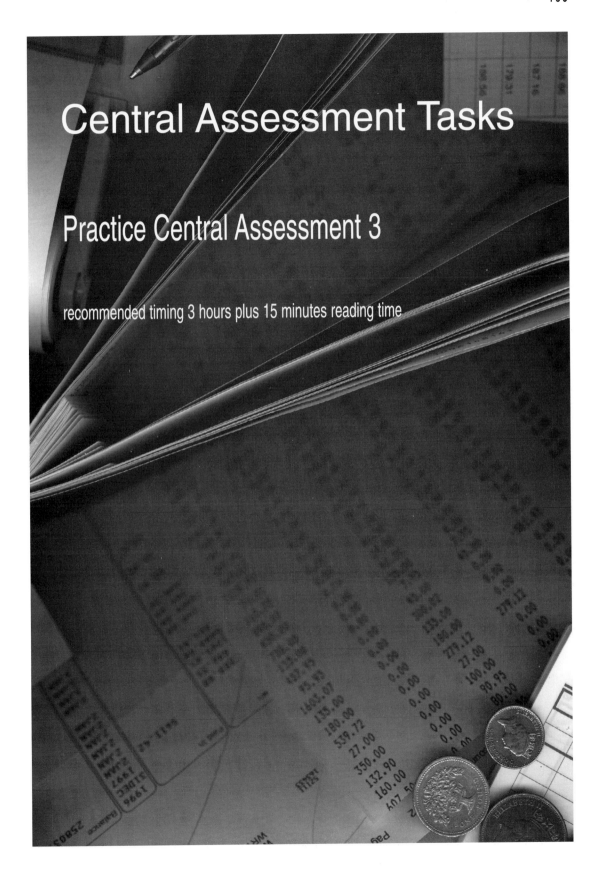

Central Assessment Tasks

Practice Central Assessment 3

recommended timing 3 hours plus 15 minutes reading time

SECTION 1

You are advised to spend approximately 55 minutes on this section

This section is in two parts.

PART A

You are advised to spend 25 minutes on this part.

Data

The accounting equation of a business is as follows:

Assets £1,200 – Liabilities £800 = Ownership interest £400

The business subsequently makes two transactions:

(1)   The business purchases on credit stock costing £120.

(2)   The business sells the stock purchased in (1) for £180 cash.

Task 1.1

(a)   Explain what is meant by "assets", "liabilities" and "ownership interest".

(b)   Explain the effect of each transaction on the elements in the balance sheet.

(c)   State the accounting equation for the business after the two transactions have taken place.

(d)   Draft a simple profit and loss account for the two transactions.

(e)   Give an example of a user who might be interested in a profit and loss account. Explain how the user you have chosen might find the statement useful.

PART B

You are advised to spend 30 minutes on this part.

Data

Duncan Tweedy wishes to invest some money in one of two private companies. He has obtained the latest financial statements for Byrne Ltd and May Ltd prepared for internal purposes. As part of his decision-making process he has asked you to assess the relative profitability of the two companies. The financial statements of the companies are set out on the next page.

**Summary profit and loss account
for the year ended 30th September 20-1**

	Byrne Ltd	May Ltd
	£000	£000
Turnover	5,761	2,927
Cost of sales	2,362	966
Gross profit	3,399	1,961
Distribution costs	922	468
Administrative expenses	1,037	439
Operating profit	1,440	1,054
Interest paid and similar charges	152	40
Profit on ordinary activities before taxation	1,288	1,014
Tax on profit on ordinary activities	309	243
Profit for the financial year	979	771
Dividends	312	141
Retained profit for the financial year	667	630

Balance sheets as at 30th September 20-1

	Byrne Ltd		May Ltd	
	£000	£000	£000	£000
Fixed assets		6,188		2,725
Current assets	1,522		1,102	
Current liabilities	1,015		545	
Net current assets		507		557
Long term loan		(1,900)		(500)
		4,795		2,782
Capital and reserves				
Called up share capital: ordinary shares of £1 each		2,083		939
Profit and loss account		2,712		1,843
		4,795		2,782

You have also been given the following ratios:

	Byrne Ltd	May Ltd
Return on capital employed	21.5%	32.1%
Gross profit percentage	59.0%	67.0%
Net profit percentage	25.0%	36.0%
Earnings per share	47p	82p

Task 1.2

Prepare a report for Duncan Tweedy that:

(a)   explains the meaning of each ratio

(b)   uses each ratio to comment on the relative profitability of the companies

(c)   concludes – with reasons – which of the two companies is the more profitable

SECTION 2

You should spend about 125 minutes on this section

This section is in four parts.

PART A

You should spend about 25 minutes on this part.

Data

The Finance Director of Wood plc has asked you to prepare the draft consolidated profit and loss account for the group. The company has one subsidiary undertaking, Plank Ltd. The profit and loss accounts for the two companies, prepared for internal purposes, for the year ended 31 March 20-1 are set out below.

Profit and loss accounts for the year ended 31 March 20-1

	Wood plc	Plank Ltd
	£000	*£000*
Turnover	31,600	10,800
Cost of sales	17,000	5,600
Gross profit	14,600	5,200
Distribution costs	3,600	1,300
Administrative expenses	3,000	1,160
Dividends received from Plank Ltd	600	
Profit on ordinary activities before interest	8,600	2,740
Interest paid and similar charges	1,600	240
Profit on ordinary activities before taxation	7,000	2,500
Tax on profit on ordinary activities	2,240	740
Profit on ordinary activities after taxation	4,760	1,760
Dividends	1,500	800
Retained profit for the financial year	3,260	960

Further information:

- Wood plc acquired 75% of the ordinary share capital of Plank Ltd on 1 April 20-0.

- During the year Plank Ltd sold stock which had cost £600,000 to Wood plc for £1,000,000. All of the stock had been sold by Wood plc by the end of the year.

- Ignore any write-off of goodwill for the period.

Task 2.1

Using the pro-forma on the next page draft a consolidated profit and loss account for Wood plc and its subsidiary undertaking for the year ended 31 March 20-1.

Consolidated profit and loss account

for the year ended 31 March 20-1

£000

Turnover

Continuing operations

  Acquisitions

Discontinued operations

Cost of sales _____

Gross profit

Distribution costs

Administrative expenses

Operating profit _____

Continuing operations

  Acquisitions _____

Discontinued operations

Loss on disposal of discontinued operations

Profit on ordinary activities before interest

Interest payable _____

Profit on ordinary activities before taxation

Tax on profit on ordinary activities _____

Profit on ordinary activities after taxation

Minority interests _____

Dividends

Retained profit for the financial year ▬▬▬▬▬▬▬

PART B

You should spend about 30 minutes on this part.

Data

You have been asked to prepare a cash flow statement for Strongman Ltd for the year ended 31 March 20-1. The profit and loss account and balance sheets of Strongman Ltd are set out below.

Strongman Ltd

Profit and loss account for the year ended 31 March 20-1

	£000
Turnover	18,094
Cost of sales	9,878
Gross profit	8,216
Profit on the sale of fixed assets	186
Distribution costs	2,026
Administrative expenses	1,444
Profit on ordinary activities before interest	4,932
Interest paid and similar charges	486
Profit on ordinary activities before taxation	4,446
Tax on profit on ordinary activities	1,018
Profit for the financial year	3,428
Dividends	1,260
Retained profit for the financial year	2,168

Strongman Ltd

Balance sheets as at 31 March

	20-1		20-0	
	£000	£000	£000	£000
Fixed assets		10,732		8,150
Current assets				
Stocks	6,032		4,568	
Trade debtors	3,016		2,788	
Cash	46		–	
	9,094		7,356	

Current liabilities

Trade creditors	2,744		1,860	
Dividends payable	840		760	
Taxation	1,018		984	
Bank overdraft	–		274	
	4,602		3,878	
Net current assets		4,492		3,478
Long term loan		(6,076)		(6,648)
		9,148		4,980
Capital and reserves				
Called up share capital		5,000		3,800
Share premium		800		–
Profit and loss account		3,348		1,180
		9,148		4,980

Further information:

- A fixed asset costing £726,000 with accumulated depreciation of £346,000 was sold during the year. The total depreciation charge for the year was £1,010,000.

- All sales and purchases were on credit. Other expenses were paid for in cash.

Task 2.2

Prepare a reconciliation of operating profit to net cash flows from operating activities for Strongman Ltd for the year ended 31 March 20-1.

Task 2.3

Using the pro-forma on the next page, prepare a cash flow statement for Strongman Ltd for the year ended 31 March 20-1 in accordance with the requirements of FRS 1 (Revised).

Cash Flow Statement

for the year ended 31 March 20-1

	£000	£000
Net cash inflow from operating activities		
Returns on investments and servicing of finance		
Taxation		
Capital expenditure		
		————
Equity dividends		
Management of liquid resources		————
Financing		
Increase /(decrease) in cash		
		————

PART C

You should spend about 50 minutes on this part.

Data

You have been asked to help prepare the financial statements of Blakedown plc for the year ended 31 March 20-1. The trial balance of the company as at 31 March 20-1 is set out below.

Blakedown plc
Trial balance as at 31 March 20-1

	Debit	Credit
	£000	£000
Trade creditors		4,614
Sales		42,766
Cash at bank	370	
Interest	800	
Trade debtors	7,128	
Land - cost	10,300	
Buildings - cost	6,146	
Fixtures and fittings - cost	4,338	
Motor vehicles - cost	9,218	
Office equipment - cost	1,854	
Interim dividend	900	
Ordinary share capital		6,000
Accruals		270
Long term loan		10,000
Distribution costs	4,034	
Administrative expenses	2,702	
Profit and loss account		10,680
Prepayments	184	
Share premium		3,000
Buildings - accumulated depreciation		840
Fixtures and fittings - accumulated depreciation		1,512
Motor vehicles - accumulated depreciation		4,028
Office equipment - accumulated depreciation		764
Stock as at 1 April 20-0	9,032	
Purchases	27,682	
Provision for doubtful debts		214
	84,688	84,688

Further information:

- The authorised share capital of the company, all of which has been issued consists of ordinary shares with a nominal value of £1.

- The company paid an interim dividend of 15p per share during the year but has not provided for the proposed final dividend of 20p per share.

- The stock at close of business on 31 March 20-1 was valued at cost at £10,692,000.

- The corporation tax charge for the year has been calculated as £2,946,000.

- Additions to fixed assets were:

Motor vehicles	£2,680,000
Office equipment	£536,000

  Motor vehicles which had cost £1,950,000 and which had accumulated depreciation of £1,012,000 were disposed of during the year. There were no other additions or disposals. All of the additions and disposals have been included in the accounts as at 31 March 20-1.

  No net depreciation charges for the year have been entered into the accounts as at 31 March 20-1. The depreciation charges for the year are as follows:

	£000
Buildings	130
Fixtures and fittings	434
Motor vehicles	1,296
Office equipment	370

  The land has been revalued by professional valuers at £12,000,000. The revaluation is to be included in the financial statements for the year ended 31 March 20-1.

  Legal proceedings have been started against Blakedown Ltd because of faulty products supplied to a customer. The company's lawyers advise that it is probable that the entity will be found liable for damages of £500,000.

Task 2.4

Using the pro-forma on the next page make the necessary journal entries as a result of the further information given above. Dates and narratives are not required.

Notes

(1) You must show any workings relevant to these adjustments.

(2) Ignore any effect of these adjustments on the tax charge for the year given above.

Task 2.5

Using the pro-forma on the page after next, draft a note to the accounts showing movements in tangible fixed assets, as far as the information given allows.

Task 2.6

Explain your treatment of the probable damages arising from the legal proceedings. Refer, where relevant, to accounting standards.

JOURNAL		
	Dr £	Cr £

	Land £000	Buildings £000	Fixtures & fittings £000	Motor vehicles £000	Office equipment £000	Total £000
Cost/Valuation						
1 April 20-0						
Additions						
Revaluation						
Disposals						
31 March 20-1						
Accumulated depreciation						
1 April 20-0						
Charge for year						
Disposals						
31 March 20-1						
Net book value						
31 March 20-1						
31 March 20-0						

PART D

You should spend about 20 minutes on this part.

Data

Sandra and Camille were in partnership selling books. On 1 April 20-1 they admitted Steven into the partnership. You need to make the entries to account for the admission of Steven into the partnership. You have the following information:

(1) On 1 April 20-1 Steven paid £160,000 into the partnership. The profit sharing ratio in the old partnership was:

Sandra	7/10
Camille	3/10

The profit sharing ratio in the new partnership will be:

Sandra	6/10
Camille	2/10
Steven	2/10

The partners will be entitled to the following salaries per annum:

	£
Sandra	80,000
Camille	50,000
Steven	40,000

(2) On the day that Steven was admitted into the partnership the goodwill in the partnership was valued at £300,000. No goodwill is to be kept in the accounts of the new partnership. Adjustments for goodwill are to be made in the capital accounts of the partners.

(3) The fixed assets of the partnership were revalued at £240,000 on 1 April 20-1. The net book value of the assets that appears in the accounts at 1 April 20-1 is £140,000. The revaluation is not to be kept in the books of the partnership.

(4) The balances on the capital accounts at 31 March 20-1 were:

	£
Sandra	170,000
Camille	90,000

Task 2.7

Prepare the partners' capital accounts as at 1 April 20-1, showing entries required for the admission of Steven into the partnership.

Central Assessment Tasks

Practice Central Assessment 4

recommended timing 3 hours plus 15 minutes reading time

SECTION 1

You should spend about 55 minutes on this section.

Data

Terry Paine is deciding whether to lend some money to Russell Ltd. He has asked you to comment on the financial position of the company and to explain certain aspects of the financial statements of the company. He has given you the financial statements of Russell Ltd. They are set out below.

Russell Ltd

Profit and loss accounts for the year ended 31 March

	20-1	20-0
	£000	£000
Turnover	7,702	6,826
Cost of sales	4,004	3,550
Gross profit	3,698	3,276
Distribution costs	1,564	1,474
Administrative expenses	1,030	982
Operating profit	1,104	820
Interest paid and similar charges	92	82
Profit on ordinary activities before taxation	1,012	738
Tax on profit on ordinary activities	252	184
Profit for the financial year	760	554
Dividends	320	280
Retained profit for the financial year	440	274

Russell Ltd

Balance sheets as at 31 March

	20-1		20-0	
	£000	£000	£000	£000
Fixed assets		8,744		8,682
Current assets				
Stock	2,314		1,432	
Debtors	892		1,018	
Prepayments	46		38	
Cash at bank	74		114	
	3,326		2,602	

Current liabilities				
Trade creditors	812		784	
Accruals	62		52	
Dividends payable	320		280	
Taxation	252		184	
	1,446		1,300	
Net current assets		1,880		1,302
Long term loan		(1,200)		(1,000)
		9,424		8,984
Capitals and reserves				
Called up share capital: ordinary shares of £1 each		2,000		2,000
Profit and loss account		7,424		6,984
		9,424		8,984

Task 1.1

Write a letter to Terry Paine that includes the following:

(a) A calculation of the following ratios of Russell Ltd for each of the two years:

    (i)   Current ratio

    (ii)   Quick ratio/acid test

    (iii)   Gearing ratio

    (iv)   Interest cover

(b) An explanation of the meaning of each ratio.

(c) A comment on the financial position of Russell Ltd as shown by the ratios.

(d) A comment on the way the financial position has changed over the two years covered by the financial statements.

(e) A conclusion on whether Terry Paine should lend money to Russell Ltd. Base your conclusion only on the ratios calculated and analysis performed.

Task 1.2

Prepare notes for a meeting with Terry that answers the following questions relating to the financial statements of Russell Ltd:

(a) Why is the plant and machinery included in the fixed assets of the company classified as an 'asset' of the business?

(b) Why is the bank loan classified as a 'liability' of the business?

(c) (i)   Why is the final figure of 'retained profit for the year' in the profit and loss account not the same amount that appears as the profit and loss figure on the balance sheet of the company?

    (ii)   Is there any connection between the two figures?

SECTION 2

This section is in four parts. You are advised to spend approximately 125 minutes on this section.

PART A

You are advised to spend 15 minutes on this part.

Data

You have been asked to assist in the preparation of financial statements for Paton Ltd for the year ended 30th September 20-1. The profit and loss account and balance sheets of Paton Ltd are set out below:

Paton Ltd

Profit and loss account for the year ended 30th September 20-1

	£000
Turnover	24,732
Cost of sales	11,129
Gross profit	13,603
Profit on the sale of fixed assets	131
Distribution costs	4,921
Administrative expenses	2,875
Profit on ordinary activities before interest	5,938
Interest paid and similar charges	392
Profit on ordinary activities before taxation	5,546
Tax on profit on ordinary activities	1,821
Profit for the financial year	3,725
Dividends	1,500
Retained profit for the financial year	2,225

Paton Ltd

Balance sheet as at 30th September

	20-1 £000	20-1 £000	20-0 £000	20-0 £000
Fixed assets		13,383		9,923
Investment in MacNeal Ltd		5,000		
Current assets				
Stock	7,420		6,823	
Trade debtors	4,122		3,902	
Cash	102		1,037	
	11,644		11,762	
Current liabilities				
Trade creditors	1,855		1,432	
Dividends payable	900		700	
Taxation	1,821		1,327	
	4,576		3,459	
Net current assets		7,068		8,303
Long term loan		(5,000)		(1,500)
		20,451		16,726
Capital and reserves				
Called up share capital		10,000		9,000
Share premium		3,500		3,000
Profit and loss account		6,951		4,726
		20,451		16,726

You have been given the following further information:

• A fixed asset costing £895,000 with accumulated depreciation of £372,000 was sold in the year. The total depreciation charge for the year was £2,007,000.

• All sales and purchases were on credit. Other expenses were paid for in cash.

Task 2.1

Provide a reconciliation of operating profit to net cash flows from operating activities for Paton Ltd for the year ended 30th September 20-1.

PART B

You are advised to spend 15 minutes on this part.

Data

Paton Ltd, the company in task 2.1, has one subsidiary undertaking, MacNeal Ltd, which it acquired on the 30th September 20-1. The balance sheet of MacNeal Ltd as at 30th September is set out below:

MacNeal Ltd

Balance sheet as at 30th September 20-1

	£000	£000
Fixed assets		4,844
Current assets	3,562	
Current liabilities	1,706	
Net current assets		1,856
Long term loan		(1,900)
		4,800
Capital and reserves		
Called up share capital		1,200
Share premium		800
Profit and loss account		2,800
		4,800

You have been given the following further information:

(i) The share capital of MacNeal Ltd consists of ordinary shares of £1 each.

(ii) Paton Ltd acquired 900,000 shares in MacNeal Ltd on 30 September 20-1 at a cost of £5,000,000.

(iii) The fair value of the fixed assets of MacNeal Ltd at 30th September 20-1 was £5,844,000. The revaluation has not been reflected in the books of MacNeal Ltd.

Task 2.2

Calculate the goodwill on consolidation that arose on the acquisition of MacNeal Ltd on 30th September 20-1.

PART C

You are advised to spend 50 minutes on this part.

The directors of Mattesich Limited are to hold a board meeting next week to consider the performance of the company in the past year. They will also discuss the accounting policy for valuing fixed assets. The company accountant, who would normally prepare the documents for the meeting, is ill. He has completed the extended trial balance for the year ended 30th September 20-1 which is set out on the next page.

EXTENDED TRIAL BALANCE name: Mattesich Limited date: 30 September 20-1

Description	Trial balance Dr £000	Cr £000	Adjustments Dr £000	Cr £000	Profit and loss Dr £000	Cr £000	Balance sheet Dr £000	Cr £
Buildings - accumulated depreciation		2,731						2,731
Office equipment - accumulated depreciation		2,456						2,456
Motor vehicles - accumulated depreciation		5,502						5,502
Fixtures and fittings - accumulated depreciation		2,698						2,698
Loss on disposal of discontinued operation	473				473			
Trade creditors		2,727						2,727
Debtors	6,654						6,654	
Distribution costs	5,695		206	38	5,863			
Administrative expenses	3,337		181	49	3,469			
Land - cost	8,721						8,721	
Buildings - cost	12,873						12,873	
Office equipment - cost	6,182						6,182	
Motor vehicles - cost	11,522						11,522	
Fixtures and fittings - cost	6,913						6,913	
Interest	544				544			
Sales		40,448				40,448		
Loan		6,800						6,800
Ordinary share capital		14,000						14,000
Stock	12,973		13,482	13,482	12,973	13,482	13,482	
Profit and loss account		12,214						12,214
Accruals				387				387
Share premium		7,200						7,200
Interim dividend	2,100				2,100			
Prepayments			87				87	
Cash at bank and in hand	107						107	
Purchases	18,682				18,682			
Profit					9,826			9,826
	96,776	96,776	13,956	13,956	53,930	53,930	66,541	66,541

You have been given the following further information:

*   The share capital of the business consists of ordinary shares with nominal value of £1.

    The company paid an interim dividend of 15 pence per share this year and is proposing a final dividend of 20p per share.

*   Depreciation has been calculated on all the fixed assets of the business and has already been entered into the distribution expenses and administrative expenses ledger balances as shown on the extended trial balance.

*   The corporation tax charge for the year has been estimated at £3,813,000.

During the year the company acquired a business and also discontinued part of its operations. The results of the acquired business and the discontinued operations for the year have already been analysed by the company accountant. All of these results are included in the figures in the extended trial balance. The analysed results are set out below:

	Business acquired	Discontinued operations
	£000	£000
Turnover	2,714	1,213
Cost of sales	950	788
Gross profit	1,764	425
Distribution costs	692	234
Administration expenses	469	178
Net profit	603	13

Task 2.3

Using the pro-forma on the next page, draft a profit and loss account for the year ended 30 September 20-1 using Format 1 in accordance with the Companies Act 1985 as supplemented by FRS 3 'Reporting Financial Performance.'

Notes

You do not need to prepare any of the notes to the financial statements that are required by FRS 3.

You do not need to prepare journal entries for any additional adjustments that may be necessary as a result of the further information given above.

You do not need to do an analysis of distribution costs and administrative expenses.

Mattesich Ltd

Profit and loss account for the year ended 30th September 20-1

	£000	£000

Turnover

Continuing operations

  Acquisitions

Discontinued operations

Cost of sales

Gross profit

Distribution costs

Administrative expenses

Operating profit

Continuing operations

  Acquisitions

Discontinued operations

Loss on disposal of discontinued operations

Profit on ordinary activities before interest

Interest payable

Profit on ordinary activities before taxation

Tax on profit on ordinary activities

Profit on ordinary activities after taxation

Dividends

Retained profit for the financial year

Task 2.4

Prepare brief notes to take to the Board meeting covering the following questions from the directors:

(a)   If we decide to adopt a policy of revaluation of land and buildings, do we need to revalue all the land and buildings that we own or can some continue to be shown at historical cost?

(b)   If we do revalue land and buildings:

     (i)   What should be the carrying value at the balance sheet date?

     (ii)   What valuation basis should we adopt for our land and buildings given that they are non-specialised properties?

     (iii)   Where should we recognise any gain that is made on revaluation?

Explain your answers by reference to relevant accounting standards.

Part D

You are advised to spend 45 minutes on this part.

Data

Edwina and Winifred were in partnership selling and distributing medical equipment. On 1 October 20-0 they admitted Elsa into the partnership. You have been asked to finalise the partnership accounts for the year ended 30 September 20-1 and make the entries necessary to account for the admission of Elsa into the partnership. You have been given the following information:

1   On 1st October 20-0 Elsa paid £60,000 into the partnership. The profit sharing ratio in the old partnership was:

    Edwina   6/10
    Winifred   4/10

    The profit sharing ratio in the new partnership will be:
    Edwina   5/10
    Winifred   3/10
    Elsa   2/10

2   On the day that Elsa was admitted into the partnership, the goodwill in the partnership was valued at £200,000. No goodwill is to be kept in the accounts of the new partnership. Adjustments for goodwill are to be made in the capital accounts of the partners.

3   The accounts for the year ended 30th September 20-1 show that the partnership made a profit of £178,700.

4   Interest on capital is to be paid at a rate of 10 per cent on the balance at the year end on the capital accounts. No interest is paid on the current accounts.

5   Cash drawings during the year amounted to:

               £
    Edwina   76,500
    Winifred   55,200
    Elsa   38,700

6   The partners are entitled to the following salaries per annum:

	£
Edwina	25,000
Winifred	20,000
Elsa	20,000

The balances on the current and capital accounts at the beginning of the year, before any adjustments were made for the admission of Elsa into the partnership, were as follows:

Capital accounts:

	£
Edwina	45,000
Winifred	32,000

Current accounts:

	£
Edwina	6,200
Winifred	5,400

Task 2.5

Prepare the partners' capital accounts for the year ended 30th September 20-1 from the information provided above.

Task 2.6

Prepare an appropriation account for the partnership for the year ended 30th September 20-1.

Task 2.7

Prepare the partners' current accounts for the year ended 30th September 20-1.

notes